HOUGHTON MIFFLIN HARCOURT

Go Math!

Intensive Intervention

 **RtI Response to Intervention Tier 3 Activities**

Teacher Guide

Grade 6

INCLUDES:

- **Diagnostic Practice for Prerequisite Skills**
- **Activities for Students Needing Tier 3 Instructional Intervention**
- **Copying Masters**

Houghton
Mifflin
Harcourt

www.hmhschool.com

Printed in the U.S.A.

ISBN   978-0-544-24901-1

    4 5 6 7 8 9 10   0877   22 21 20 19 18 17 16 15 14

4500487119   A B C D E F G

Contents

Using Response to Intervention • Tier 3 Activities

Response to Intervention • Tier 3 Activities are targeted at students who are performing need one-on-one instruction to build foundational skills for grade-level success. By focusing on essential prerequisite skills and concepts, *Response to Intervention • Tier 3 Activities* prescribe instruction to prepare students for grade-level success in your mathematics program.

How do I determine if a student needs *Response to Intervention • Tier 3 Activities*?

Use the Show What You Know pages at the beginning of each chapter of the Student Edition to diagnose a student's need for intervention. Show What You Know targets the prerequisite skills necessary for success in each chapter. If a student misses a limited number of exercises, that student would benefit from *Strategic Intervention. Strategic Intervention* **is** prescribed in the Teacher Edition for each chapter. Students who miss at least half of the exercises from Show What You Know are candidates for *Intensive Intervention*. Use the prescription chart (page 4) in the *Intensive Intervention User Guide/Activity Guide* to determine whether or not a student requires *Intensive Intervention*.

Which *Response to Intervention • Tier 3* skill lessons do I assign for each chapter?

The Chapter Correlation in the *Intensive Intervention User Guide/Activity Guide* correlates the *Response to Intervention • Tier 3* skills to each chapter of your mathematics program.

Once you have identified a student as needing *Response to Intervention • Tier 3 Activities* and have determined which skills cover prerequisites for that chapter, use the Pre-Assess activities for each recommended skill to identify the specific, intensive prerequisite skills the student needs to develop. The Pre-Assess activities, which appear at the beginning of the teacher pages for each skill lesson, will help you determine which skills will help the student succeed in each chapter.

What materials and resources do I need for *Response to Intervention • Tier 3*?

Response to Intervention • Tier 3 resources include the Teacher Guide and Skill Packs for each grade level. The teaching strategies may require the use of common classroom manipulatives or easily gathered classroom objects. Since these activities are designed for only those students who show weaknesses in their skill development, the quantity of materials will be small. For many activities, you may substitute materials, such as paper squares for tiles, coins for two-color counters, and so on.

How are the skill lessons structured?

Each skill lesson includes two student pages and two pages of teacher support in the Teacher Guide. Each lesson begins with Learn the Math, a guided page that provides a model or an explanation of the skill. The second part of the lesson is Do the Math, a selection of exercises that provide practice and may be completed independently, with a partner, or with teacher direction. Students who have difficulty with the Do the Math exercises may benefit from the Alternative Teaching Strategy activity provided in the Teacher Guide.

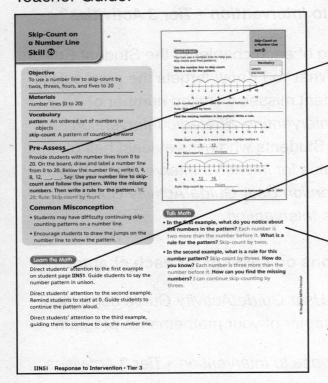

Pre-Assess allows teachers to determine which prerequisite skills the student needs to develop.

Learn the Math provides guided instruction of the skill through a model or an explanation.

Talk Math questions allow teachers to guide students' understanding and allow students to summarize their learning.

The **Alternative Teaching Strategy** provides another way for the student to acquire the skill by using a hands-on format. The activity is useful for different types of learners.

Do the Math provides practice, allowing students to demonstrate mastery of prerequisite skills.

The **Check** question allows students to demonstrate their understanding.

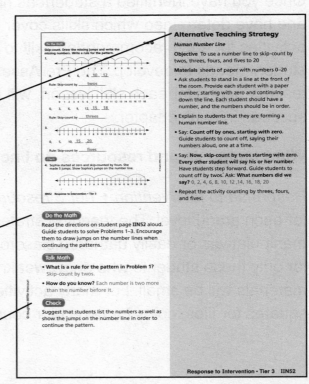

How can I assess students' understanding?

Use the Talk Math questions in the Teacher Guide to encourage students to verbalize their thinking and understanding as they complete the skill lesson. The Check at the end of the Do the Math section also provides students an opportunity to demonstrate their understanding and summarize their learning. These verbal and written responses allow teachers to assess students' knowledge of these prerequisite skills and determine if the students require further instruction with the Alternative Teaching Strategy.

What support is provided for students who need language support?

The first student page of every lesson provides examples and visuals carefully selected to illustrate the mathematics and promote discussion. Words on the student pages are deliberately kept to a minimum so that all students can be successful, regardless of English language acquisition. Language support for math vocabulary is provided in the Teacher Guide for most lessons. Additional support for vocabulary development can be found online at the animated Multimedia eGlossary at **www.hmhschool.com**.

How can I organize my classroom and schedule time for intervention?

You may want to set up a Math Skill Center with a record folder for each student. Assign appropriate skills in each student's folder, then allow students to work through the intervention materials, record the date of completion, and place the completed work in their folders for your review.

Students might visit the Math Skill Center for a specified time during the day, two or three times a week, or during free time. You may wish to assign students a partner, assign a small group to work together, or work with individuals one-on-one.

Place Value Through Hundred Thousands Skill ❶

Objective

To model, read, write, and identify the place value of whole numbers through hundred thousands

Materials

base-ten blocks

Vocabulary

digit Any one of the ten symbols 0, 1, 2, 3, 4, 5, 6, 7, 8, or 9 used to write numbers

place value The value of a digit in a number, based on the location of the digit

expanded form A way to write numbers by showing the value of each digit

standard form A way to write numbers by using digits

word form A way to write numbers by using words

Pre-Assess

Ask students to identify the value of each digit in the number 862,435. 800,000; 60,000; 2,000; 400; 30; 5 Then have students write the number in standard form, expanded form, and word form. 862,435; 800,000 + 60,000 + 2,000 + 400 + 30 + 5; eight hundred sixty-two thousand, four hundred thirty-five

Common Misconception

• Students may be confused when working with a number that includes the digit 0.

• To correct this, remind students that although they should record the 0 in the place-value chart and when writing a number in standard form, they do not need to write or represent 0 in word form or expanded form.

Learn the Math

Read the first problem on student page **IIN1**. Ask students to identify the number of thousands,

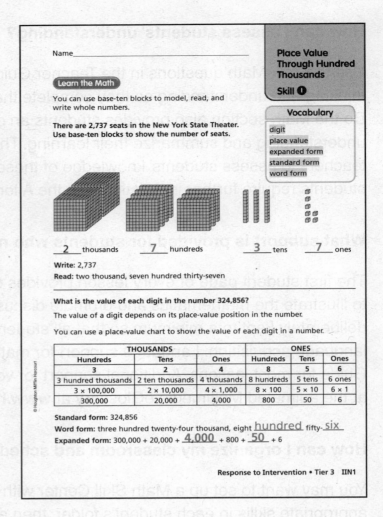

Learn the Math

You can use base-ten blocks to model, read, and write whole numbers.

There are 2,737 seats in the New York State Theater. Use base-ten blocks to show the number of seats.

Vocabulary
digit
place value
expanded form
standard form
word form

__2__ thousands   __7__ hundreds   __3__ tens   __7__ ones

Write: 2,737
Read: two thousand, seven hundred thirty-seven

What is the value of each digit in the number 324,856?

The value of a digit depends on its place-value position in the number.

You can use a place-value chart to show the value of each digit in a number.

THOUSANDS			ONES		
Hundreds	Tens	Ones	Hundreds	Tens	Ones
3	2	4	8	5	6
3 hundred thousands	2 ten thousands	4 thousands	8 hundreds	5 tens	6 ones
3 × 100,000	2 × 10,000	4 × 1,000	8 × 100	5 × 10	6 × 1
300,000	20,000	4,000	800	50	6

Standard form: 324,856
Word form: three hundred twenty-four thousand, eight __hundred__ fifty- __six__
Expanded form: 300,000 + 20,000 + __4,000__ + 800 + __50__ + 6

Response to Intervention • Tier 3   IIN1

hundreds, tens, and ones represented by the model. Direct student's attention to how the number is written and read. Then read the next problem. Discuss the general format of the place-value chart with students. Ask: **What does each column in the chart represent?** the different place value positions: ones, tens, hundreds, thousands, ten thousands, and hundred thousands

Talk Math

• In 324,856, why do you multiply the 3 by 100,000 to find its value? because the 3 is in the hundred thousands place

• What is the value of the 3 in 324,856? 3 × 100,000 = 300,000, so the value is 300,000.

Repeat these questions to identify the value of each digit. Then help students see how the place-value chart is useful for writing the standard form, word form, and expanded form of a number.

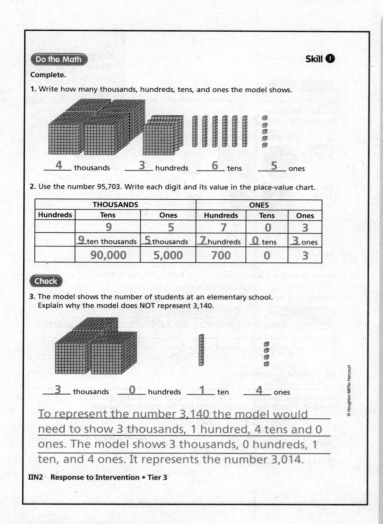

Do the Math · Complete. · Skill ❶

1. Write how many thousands, hundreds, tens, and ones the model shows.

__4__ thousands __3__ hundreds __6__ tens __5__ ones

2. Use the number 95,703. Write each digit and its value in the place-value chart.

THOUSANDS			ONES		
Hundreds	Tens	Ones	Hundreds	Tens	Ones
	9	5	7	0	3
	9 ten thousands	5 thousands	7 hundreds	0 tens	3 ones
	90,000	5,000	700	0	3

Check

3. The model shows the number of students at an elementary school. Explain why the model does NOT represent 3,140.

__3__ thousands __0__ hundreds __1__ ten __4__ ones

To represent the number 3,140 the model would need to show 3 thousands, 1 hundred, 4 tens and 0 ones. The model shows 3 thousands, 0 hundreds, 1 ten, and 4 ones. It represents the number 3,014.

IIN2   Response to Intervention • Tier 3

© Houghton Mifflin Harcourt

Do the Math

Guide students as they complete student page **IIN2**. Direct students' attention to the model in Problem 1 and help them identify the number of thousands, hundreds, tens, and ones shown.

Talk Math

• In Problem 2, how many tens are there in 95,703? zero

• Do you need to include the 0 when you write the number in expanded or word form? no

Check

How does knowing the value of each digit help you write the number in expanded form? In expanded form, you write the value of each digit in order with addition signs between each value. So if I know the values are 3,000, 10, and 4, I know that the number is written 3,000 + 10 + 4.

Alternative Teaching Strategy

Model the Base-Ten System

Objective To understand the place-value structure of the base-ten number system

Materials base-ten blocks, place-value charts

• Review with students that the value of a digit depends on the location of the digit in the place-value chart. Say: **In the base-ten number system, each place value is ten times the place value to the right.**

• Have students work in pairs. Provide each pair of students a set of base-ten blocks (thousands, hundreds, tens, and ones). Ask Students to model the number 1.

• Then ask students to model 10 ones. Ask: **How many tens are equal to 10 ones?** 1 ten Have students trade the 10 ones for 1 ten.

• Ask students to model 10 tens. **How many hundreds are equal to 10 tens?** 1 hundred Have students trade the 10 tens for 1 hundred.

• Write the number 555,555 on the board. Have students record the number in a place-value chart.

• Remind students that they can multiply each digit by its place value to find its value in the number.

• **How many ones are there?** 5 **What is the value of the 5 in the ones place?** $5 \times 1 = 5$ **How many tens are there?** 5 **What is the value of the 5 in the tens place?** $5 \times 10 = 50$ **How many hundreds are there?** 5 **What is the value of the 5 in the hundreds place?** $5 \times 100 = 500$ **How many thousands are there?** 5 **What is the value of the 5 in the thousands place?** $5 \times 1,000 = 5,000$ **What is the value of the 5 in the ten thousands place?** $5 \times 10,000 = 50,000$ **What is the value of the 5 in the hundred thousands place?** $5 \times 100,000 = 500,000$

Objective
To compare and order whole numbers using base-ten blocks, place value, and number lines

Materials
base-ten blocks

Vocabulary
equal to (=) Having the same value

greater than (>) A symbol used to compare two numbers with the greater number given first

less than (<) A symbol used to compare two numbers with the lesser number given first

place value The value of a digit in a number, based on the location of the digit

Pre-Assess
Display the following sets of numbers. Ask students to write the numbers in order from *least* to *greatest*.

1. 6,074; 7,604; 7,460 6,074; 7,460; 7,604

2. 40,527,074; 40,257,707; 4,752,005
   4,752,005; 40,257,707; 40,527,074

Ask students to write these sets of numbers in order from *greatest* to *least.*

3. 356, 353, 653 653, 356, 353
4. 12,389; 11,298; 11,931 12,389; 11,931; 11,298

Common Misconception

• Students may confuse the *greater than* and *less than* symbols.

• To correct this, remind students that the symbol opens to the greater number. You may wish to illustrate the symbol as the mouth of an animal (such as an alligator) to emphasize this idea to students.

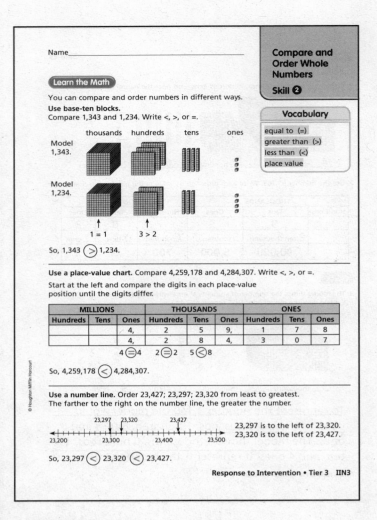

Read the first problem on student page **IIN3**. Ask students to identify the number of thousands, hundreds, tens, and ones in the numbers 1,343 and 1,234. Then model how to compare each place-value position. Guide students to conclude that 1,343 is greater than 1,234.

Read the second problem. Explain the process for using place value to compare numbers. Ask questions to help students compare the digits in each place-value position. For the third problem, instruct students to compare points on the number line before answering.

Talk Math

• **How are numbers organized on a number line?** They increase in value as you move to the right.

• **Is 23,297 to the left or right of 23,320?** to the left

• **What does this tell you?** 23,297 is less than 23,320

Use similar questions to compare the numbers 23,427 and 23,320.

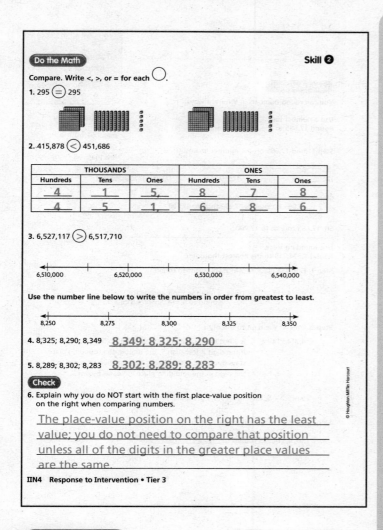

Compare. Write <, >, or = for each ◯.

1. 295 ⬚=⬚ 295

2. 415,878 ⬚<⬚ 451,686

THOUSANDS			ONES		
Hundreds	Tens	Ones	Hundreds	Tens	Ones
4	1	5,	8	7	8
4	5	1,	6	8	6

3. 6,527,117 ⬚>⬚ 6,517,710

6,510,000   6,520,000   6,530,000   6,540,000

Use the number line below to write the numbers in order from greatest to least.

8,250   8,275   8,300   8,325   8,350

4. 8,325; 8,290; 8,349   <u>8,349; 8,325; 8,290</u>

5. 8,289; 8,302; 8,283   <u>8,302; 8,289; 8,283</u>

Check

6. Explain why you do NOT start with the first place-value position on the right when comparing numbers.

<u>The place-value position on the right has the least value; you do not need to compare that position unless all of the digits in the greater place values are the same.</u>

IIN4   Response to Intervention • Tier 3

© Houghton Mifflin Harcourt

Do the Math

Ask students to discuss what they have learned about each method of comparing numbers. Then work with students to complete student page **IIN4**.

Talk Math

• **When might you need to compare numbers?**
  Possible answer: to compare prices

• **When might you need to order numbers?**
  Possible answer: to list players' scores in order

Check

Point out that the numbers 900,001 and 100,009 have the same number of digits. Show students that 900,001 is a much greater number, but if they start at the right instead of the left, they will mistakenly find 100,009 to be greater.

© Houghton Mifflin Harcourt

Alternative Teaching Strategy

Model, Compare, and Order Numbers

Objective To compare and order numbers using base-ten blocks

Materials base-ten blocks, index cards

• Distribute base-ten blocks and index cards to students. Ask each student to write a 4-digit number on his or her card.

• Review with students how to model a 4-digit number using base-ten blocks. Ask: **How would you model the number you have written on your card?** Invite a volunteer to explain how he or she would make the model.

• Direct students to model their 4-digit numbers and share their models with the class.

• Use questions to guide students to compare the numbers shown by the models. Ask: **How can you compare the numbers?** Compare the value of the blocks in each place-value position. **Where will you start comparing?** Start with the greatest place value, going from left to right. **How will you know which number is greater?** I keep comparing the value of the blocks until the values are different. Write two of the 4-digit numbers on the board and ask a volunteer to write >, <, or = to compare them.

• Invite a third student to share his or her model. Repeat the process for comparing this model with the other two models. Then challenge students to write the three 4-digit numbers in order from least to greatest. Ask: **Which number is greatest? Which is least? How do you know?** Answers will vary. Have students use place-value terms to explain their reasoning.

• Invite a new pair of students to share their models and 4-digit numbers. Repeat the activity.

Round Whole Numbers
Skill 3

Objective
To round 4-digit numbers to the nearest thousand using a number line and rounding rules

Materials
number line

Vocabulary
equal to (=) Having the same value

greater than (>) A symbol used to compare two numbers with the greater number given first

less than (<) A symbol used to compare two numbers with the lesser number given first

number line A line on which numbers can be located

round To replace a number with another number that tells about how many or how much

Pre-Assess
Challenge students to round each of the following numbers to the nearest thousand: 1,391; 5,288; 3,840; 7,456. 1,000; 5,000; 4,000; 7,000

Common Misconception
- Students may round to the wrong place.

- To correct this, remind students that when they round to the nearest thousand, they are deciding whether the digit in the thousands place should increase by 1 or stay the same.

- You may also wish to clarify that regardless of whether the thousands digit changes, the remaining digits (to the right of the rounding digit) will all be replaced with zeros.

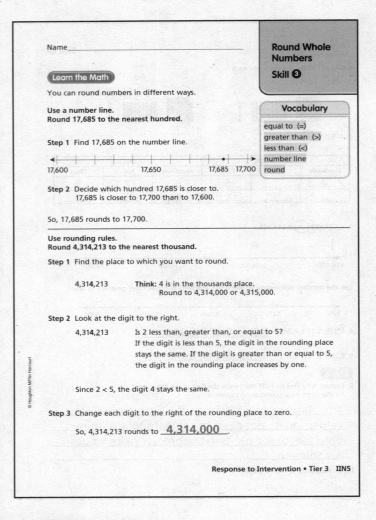

Name_____

Round Whole Numbers
Skill 3

Learn the Math
You can round numbers in different ways.

Use a number line.
Round 17,685 to the nearest hundred.

Step 1 Find 17,685 on the number line.

17,600   17,650   17,685 17,700

Step 2 Decide which hundred 17,685 is closer to.
17,685 is closer to 17,700 than to 17,600.

So, 17,685 rounds to 17,700.

Use rounding rules.
Round 4,314,213 to the nearest thousand.

Step 1 Find the place to which you want to round.

4,314,213   Think: 4 is in the thousands place.
Round to 4,314,000 or 4,315,000.

Step 2 Look at the digit to the right.

4,314,213   Is 2 less than, greater than, or equal to 5?
If the digit is less than 5, the digit in the rounding place stays the same. If the digit is greater than or equal to 5, the digit in the rounding place increases by one.

Since 2 < 5, the digit 4 stays the same.

Step 3 Change each digit to the right of the rounding place to zero.

So, 4,314,213 rounds to **4,314,000**

Vocabulary
equal to (=)
greater than (>)
less than (<)
number line
round

Response to Intervention • Tier 3   IIN5

Learn the Math
Read the first problem on student page **IIN5**. Help students identify the value of each tick mark on the number line. Then discuss which hundred 17,685 is closer to: 17,600 or 17,700. Direct students' attention to the second problem. Discuss the rounding rules and the steps to use when using rounding rules.

Talk Math
- **For the first problem, to which place are you rounding 17,685?** the hundreds place

- **For the second problem, what do you need to know in order to round?** whether the value of the digit in the hundreds place is less than, equal to, or greater than 5

For the second problem, emphasize the need to write zeros in place of all of the other digits to the right of the thousands place.

© Houghton Mifflin Harcourt

Round each number to the place value of the underlined digit.

1. 9<u>2</u>1
   920

2. <u>4</u>69
   500

3. 2,8<u>7</u>6
   2,880

4. 5,<u>1</u>99
   5,200

5. <u>3</u>,321
   3,000

6. 13,<u>8</u>01
   13,800

7. 18,<u>7</u>11
   18,700

8. 1<u>6</u>,847
   17,000

9. 215,2<u>9</u>3
   215,290

10. 494,<u>5</u>34
    494,500

11. 99<u>2</u>,429
    992,000

12. 1,813,42<u>9</u>
    1,813,430

13. 6,719,2<u>1</u>0
    6,719,200

14. 5,20<u>3</u>,112
    5,203,000

Check

15. Explain how to round 1,670 to the nearest thousand.
    The number in the thousands place is 1, so I will round to 1,000 or 2,000. The digit in the hundreds place is 6. 6 > 5, so the digit in the rounding place increases by 1. I write zeros for each digit to the right of the rounding place. So, 1,670 rounds to 2,000.

Do the Math

Help students identify the place value of the underlined digit for each problem on student page IIN6.

Talk Math

- **What is the first thing you should look for on each problem?** find which digit is underlined and which place value it represents

- **When you use place value to round a number, what must be true in order for you to round up?** the digit to the right of the rounding place must be 5 or greater

Check

Ask: **How do you know how many zeros to write when you round 1,670?** I change all of the digits to the right of the digit in the rounding place to zeros. I am rounding to the thousands place, so there are three zeros.

Alternative Teaching Strategy
Rounding 4-Digit Numbers

Objective To practice rounding 4-digit numbers to the nearest thousand

Materials 11 pieces of paper, each with one of the following numbers: 0; 1,000; 2,000; 3,000; 4,000; 5,000; 6,000; 7,000; 8,000; 9,000; 10,000; index cards, each one with a different 4-digit number; 11 boxes

- Invite students to help you place 11 boxes in a line and use the paper signs to label them from 0 to 10,000, in order from least to greatest. Tell students that for this activity, they will be rounding to the thousands place.

- Shuffle the index cards and lay them in one stack face down.

- Have students take turns choosing a card from the stack. Ask them to read the number aloud and show the card to the class. Then challenge them to identify the two boxes that the 4-digit number is between.

- Ask: **To which place are you rounding?** the thousands place

- Ask questions to guide students to round the number:

    Which digit is in the hundreds place?
    Is the digit in the hundreds place less than, greater than, or equal to 5?
    Should you round down or round up?
    In which box will you place your card?

- As you ask questions, allow time for students to discuss their thought process and revise their answers, if necessary.

- When students feel confident they have arrived at the correct answer, have them place their card in the appropriate box. Then call on the next student.

- When all the cards have been selected and distributed, have students look at the cards in each box and discuss any patterns they see.

Add and Subtract 4-Digit Numbers
Skill ❹

Objective
To add and subtract 4-digit numbers

Materials
place-value charts, base-ten blocks

Pre-Assess

Provide students with place-value charts. Write the following addition problem on the board:

$$2,486$$
$$+ 5,137$$

Ask students to write the problem in their place-value chart and identify the digits in the ones, tens, hundreds, and thousands place for each number. Ask: **What do you do first?** Add the ones. **How many ones are there?** 6 + 7 = 13 **Do you need to regroup?** yes **How do you know?** There are more than 9 ones, so I regroup 10 ones as 1 ten. Allow students to work independently to record the number of ones and tens. They should continue to work independently to find the sum. 7,623

Repeat, using the same type of questions, for the following subtraction problem:

$$6,162$$
$$- 2,486$$
$$3,676$$

Common Misconception

- Students may forget to record the new number of tens, hundreds, or thousands after regrouping to subtract.

- To correct this, have students model subtraction with base-ten blocks. Point out that when they regroup 1 ten as 10 ones, there are 10 more ones in the ones column and 1 less ten in the tens column.

- To reinforce this connection, have them record each step in a place-value chart after they model it.

Name_____

Add and Subtract 4-Digit Numbers

Skill ❹

Learn the Math

Add. 3,847 + 1,258

Step 1	Step 2	Step 3	Step 4
Add the ones.	Add the tens.	Add the hundreds.	Add the thousands.
Regroup 15 ones as 1 ten 5 ones.	Regroup 10 tens as 1 hundred 0 tens.	Regroup 11 hundreds as 1 thousand 1 hundred.	
$\begin{array}{r} 1 \\ 3,847 \\ + 1,258 \\ \hline 5 \end{array}$	$\begin{array}{r} 1\;1 \\ 3,847 \\ + 1,258 \\ \hline 05 \end{array}$	$\begin{array}{r} 1\;1\;1 \\ 3,847 \\ + 1,258 \\ \hline 105 \end{array}$	$\begin{array}{r} 1\;1\;1 \\ 3,847 \\ + 1,258 \\ \hline 5,105 \end{array}$

So, 3,847 + 1,258 = __5,105__ .

Subtract. 6,138 − 3,249

Step 1	Step 2	Step 3	Step 4
Subtract the ones.	Subtract the tens.	Subtract the hundreds.	Subtract the thousands.
Since 9 > 8, regroup 3 tens 8 ones as 2 tens 18 ones.	Since 4 > 2, regroup 1 hundred 2 tens as 0 hundreds 12 tens.	Since 2 > 0, regroup 6 thousands 0 hundreds as 5 thousands 10 hundreds.	
$\begin{array}{r} 2\,18 \\ 6,13\cancel{8} \\ - 3,249 \\ \hline 9 \end{array}$	$\begin{array}{r} 12 \\ 0\,\cancel{2}18 \\ 6,\cancel{1}\cancel{3}\cancel{8} \\ - 3,249 \\ \hline 89 \end{array}$	$\begin{array}{r} 1012 \\ 5\,\cancel{2}18 \\ \cancel{6},\cancel{1}\cancel{3}\cancel{8} \\ - 3,249 \\ \hline 889 \end{array}$	$\begin{array}{r} 1012 \\ 5\,\cancel{2}18 \\ \cancel{6},\cancel{1}\cancel{3}\cancel{8} \\ - 3,249 \\ \hline 2,889 \end{array}$

So, 6,138 − 3,249 = __2,889__ .

Learn the Math

Read the first problem on student page **IIN7**. Guide students through each step, asking: **Why is regrouping necessary?** The sum of the digits is more than 9. Emphasize the importance of recording the regrouped ten, hundred, and thousand. Direct students' attention to the second problem. Discuss each step, reminding students to subtract from right to left.

Talk Math

- **When you regroup 1 ten as 10 ones, what do you need to record?** the new number of ones and the new number of tens

- **How can you tell whether you need to regroup to subtract?** I need to regroup if the number I am subtracting is greater than the number I am subtracting from.

Do the Math

Find the sum or difference.

1. $\begin{array}{r} 5,424 \\ +\ 1,597 \\ \hline 7,021 \end{array}$

2. $\begin{array}{r} 1,681 \\ +\ 1,299 \\ \hline 2,980 \end{array}$

3. $\begin{array}{r} 3,881 \\ +\ 2,325 \\ \hline 6,206 \end{array}$

4. $\begin{array}{r} 1,294 \\ +\ 6,468 \\ \hline 7,762 \end{array}$

5. $\begin{array}{r} 6,093 \\ -\ 2,470 \\ \hline 3,623 \end{array}$

6. $\begin{array}{r} 1,411 \\ +\ 1,027 \\ \hline 2,438 \end{array}$

7. $\begin{array}{r} 8,629 \\ -\ 3,859 \\ \hline 4,770 \end{array}$

8. $\begin{array}{r} 5,726 \\ +\ 3,618 \\ \hline 9,344 \end{array}$

Check

9. Look at the problem below. What is the missing number if you do NOT need to regroup to subtract? Explain.

$\begin{array}{r} 7,35\blacksquare \\ -\ 4,148 \\ \hline \end{array}$

<u>The missing number is 8 or 9, because you can</u>
<u>subtract 8 from 8 or 9 without regrouping.</u>

IIN8 Response to Intervention • Tier 3

© Houghton Mifflin Harcourt

Do the Math

Help students work through the problems on student page **IIN8**. Remind students to work from right to left and regroup when necessary.

Talk Math

- **Why are the problems written vertically?** It is easier to add and subtract when the digits are lined up by place value.

- **Why do you work from right to left?** So you can regroup to or from the greater place-value position.

Check

Ask: **Why is the answer not a number less than 8?** You cannot subtract 8 ones from less than 8 ones. You would have to regroup a ten to have more ones.

Alternative Teaching Strategy

Add to Subtract

Objective To use addition to find a difference

- Explain to students that an alternative way to find a difference is to count up from the smaller number to the greater number. You count by ones, tens, hundreds, and then thousands. After you count up, you add the values you counted to find the difference.

$$\begin{array}{r} 4,600 \\ -\ 2,349 \\ \hline \end{array}$$

Step 1
Start with the smaller number, 2,349. Count up by ones to the nearest ten.

$\begin{array}{r} 2,349 \\ +\ ①\ \\ \hline 2,350 \end{array}$

Step 2
Next, count up by tens to the nearest hundred.

$\begin{array}{r} 2,350 \\ +\ ㊿\ \\ \hline 2,400 \end{array}$

Step 3
Count up by hundreds to the number of hundreds in the greater number. The greater number is 4,600, so add 200.

$\begin{array}{r} 2,400 \\ +\ ⓧ200 \\ \hline 2,600 \end{array}$

Step 4
Count up by thousands to the greater number.

$\begin{array}{r} 2,600 \\ +2,000 \\ \hline 4,600 \end{array}$

Step 5
Circle the numbers you added to count up. Then, add the circled numbers to find the difference.

$\begin{array}{r} 2,000 \\ 200 \\ 50 \\ +\ 1 \\ \hline 2,251 \end{array}$

- Say: **The difference of 4,600 and 2,349 is 2,251.**

Multiplication and Division Facts
Skill ❺

Objective
To use strategies to learn multiplication and division facts

Materials
triangle flash cards, grid paper

Vocabulary
array An arrangement of objects in rows and columns

Pre-Assess

Ask students to find the product or quotient of the problems below. Invite students to share their problem-solving strategies.

$6 \times 9 = \underline{54}$
$8 \times 7 = \underline{56}$
$5 \times 6 = \underline{30}$
$49 \div 7 = \underline{7}$
$30 \div 6 = \underline{5}$
$60 \div 10 = \underline{6}$

Common Misconception

- Students may not have memorized basic facts to 5, and thus may write incorrect products or quotients when using strategies to learn facts from 6 to 12.

- To correct this, guide students to practice basic multiplication and division facts to 5. Provide triangle flash cards on which students can record fact families to 5. For example, students may record 3, 5, and 15, writing one number in each corner of the triangle with the greatest number at the triangle's apex. Cards can be used to practice all related facts in the family: $3 \times 5 = 15$, $5 \times 3 = 15$, $15 \div 5 = 3$, $15 \div 3 = 5$.

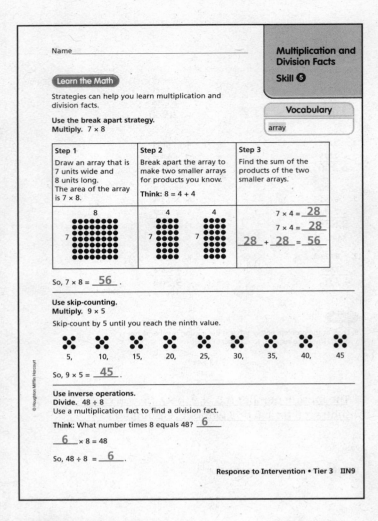

Learn the Math

Read the first problem on student page **IIN9** and guide students through each of the steps. Remind students that an array is an arrangement of objects in rows and columns. It may help students to model the process. Instruct students to draw a 7 by 8 array on grid paper and cut it in half to make two 7 by 4 arrays. Ask students to write the multiplication fact for each array, then place the two arrays together and write the product of 7 × 8.

Talk Math

- **Why do you cut the 7 by 8 array in half?** I am making two 7 by 4 arrays in order to model 7 × 4 two times.

- **Look at the groups of counters in the second problem. How many counters are in each group?** 5 **How many groups are there?** 9 **How many counters are there in all?** 45 **What multiplication fact does this show?** 9 × 5 = 45

Do the Math

Skill 5

Find the product. Show the strategy you used. Strategies will vary.

1. $7 \times 7 =$ __49__
2. $8 \times 5 =$ __40__

3. $6 \times 9 =$ __54__
4. $10 \times 3 =$ __30__

5. $7 \times 5 =$ __35__
6. $11 \times 4 =$ __44__

Find the quotient. Show the strategy you used. Strategies will vary.

7. $42 \div 6 =$ __7__
8. $81 \div 9 =$ __9__

9. $7\overline{)63}$ → 9
10. $5\overline{)50}$ → 10

11. $8\overline{)24}$ → 3
12. $9\overline{)36}$ → 4

Check

13. What strategy did you use to solve Problem 8? Why did you choose that strategy?

Possible answer: I used inverse operations. Since I know that $9 \times 9 = 81$, I also know that $81 \div 9 = 9$

IIN10 **Response to Intervention • Tier 3**

Do the Math

Call on volunteers to explain the different strategies they have learned. Then guide students to complete the problems on student page **IIN10**.

Talk Math

• **In Problem 6, suppose you know that $11 \times 2 = 22$. How can you use this fact to find 11×4?** I can draw two 11 by 2 arrays, find the products, and add them together.

• **In Problem 10, how can counting back from 50 by fives help you find $50 \div 5$?** I can count back by fives until I reach 0. The number of times I count back is the quotient: 10.

Check

Ask: **How can you check that your answer to a problem is correct?** I can use a different strategy and see if I get the same answer.

Alternative Teaching Strategy

Use a Multiplication Table

Objective To find products and quotients using a multiplication table

Materials blank multiplication tables (12 by 12)

• Distribute blank multiplication tables to pairs of students. Draw a large multiplication table on the board and review its basic format. Then model labeling rows and columns 0–12. Instruct students to follow your example on their own tables.

• Write 1×1 on the board. Ask: **What is the product of 1×1?** 1 Ask students to find row 1 and column 1. Guide them to look across and down to find the space where the product 1×1 belongs. Ask students to record the product in that space.

• Ask pairs to complete the multiplication table with facts to 5, including 0.

• Next, assign each pair of students one number from 6–12. Ask students to find and record all of the multiplication facts that include their number. Ask: **What are some strategies you might use to help you?** Possible answers: break apart strategy, arrays, inverse operations, model with counters

• Invite pairs to the board to record the facts for their assigned number in the large multiplication table. Ask students to write each set of facts as they are recorded so that each pair's table is complete.

• Write 6×7 on the board. Ask: **How can you use your table to find the product?** Look across row 6 and down column 7 to find the number where the row and column meet. This is the product of 6 and 7. **What is the product?** 42

• Now write $33 \div 3$ on the board. Guide students through the process of finding column 3 and looking down to find 33. Instruct them to look left across the row. Ask: **What is the quotient?** 11

• Repeat with other multiplication and division facts.

Objective
To use a number line to practice addition, subtraction, multiplication, and division facts

Materials
number line

Vocabulary
number line A line on which numbers can be located

Pre-Assess

Show students a number line labeled from 0–50. Ask students to explain how to use the number line to find the sum, difference, product, or quotient of the problems below.

1. 20 + 5 = __25__
   Count 5 spaces to the right of 20.
2. 41 – 10 = __31__
   Start at 41. Make 10 jumps to the left.
3. 7 × 6 = __42__
   Start at 0. Make 7 jumps of 6
4. 48 ÷ 8 = __6__
   Start at 48. Make 8 jumps to the left until you reach 0. Count the number of jumps.

Common Misconception

- Students may not remember which way to move along a number line for a particular operation.

- To correct this, remind students that the numbers increase as you move to the right on a number line. Explain that since addition and multiplication are operations that increase number values, you move to the right. Subtraction and division are the opposites of addition and multiplication, so you move to the left.

The first problem on student page **IIN11** shows addition. Remind students that the numbers on a number line increase as you go to the right.

IIN11   Response to Intervention • Tier 3

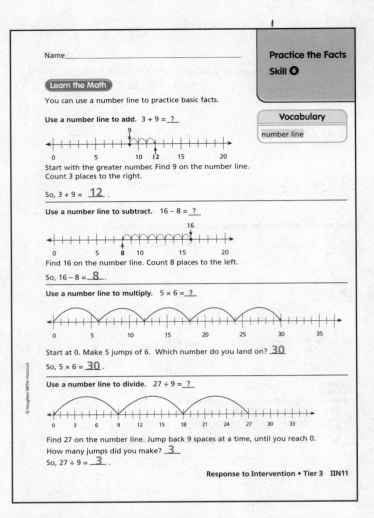

Learn the Math

You can use a number line to practice basic facts.

Use a number line to add. 3 + 9 = __?__

Start with the greater number. Find 9 on the number line. Count 3 places to the right.

So, 3 + 9 = __12__ .

Use a number line to subtract.   16 – 8 = __?__

Find 16 on the number line. Count 8 places to the left.

So, 16 – 8 = __8__ .

Use a number line to multiply.   5 × 6 = __?__

Start at 0. Make 5 jumps of 6. Which number do you land on? __30__

So, 5 × 6 = __30__ .

Use a number line to divide.   27 ÷ 9 = __?__

Find 27 on the number line. Jump back 9 spaces at a time, until you reach 0. How many jumps did you make? __3__

So, 27 ÷ 9 = __3__ .

Vocabulary
number line

Response to Intervention • Tier 3   IIN11

For addition of two numbers, find the greater addend on the number line. Then count the number of places to the right equal to the other addend.

For subtraction, find the minuend on the number line, then count the number of places to the left equal to the subtrahend. Students may find it easier to do the second problem if they first label all numbers on the line.

Assist students with using a number line to find a product. Explain the method of starting at 0 and making jumps to the right.

For division using a number line, always start at the number that is the dividend, make jumps to the left, and end at 0. Have students count the number of jumps made.

Talk Math

- **When adding or multiplying numbers, in which direction do you move along the number line?** to the right

- **When subtracting or dividing, in which direction do you move along the number line?** to the left

© Houghton Mifflin Harcourt

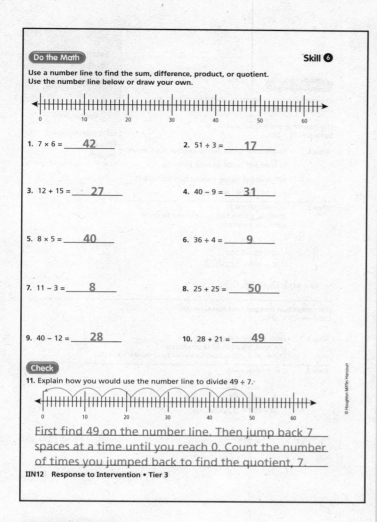

Do the Math

Use a number line to find the sum, difference, product, or quotient.
Use the number line below or draw your own.

Skill **6**

1. 7 × 6 = __42__   2. 51 ÷ 3 = __17__

3. 12 + 15 = __27__   4. 40 − 9 = __31__

5. 8 × 5 = __40__   6. 36 ÷ 4 = __9__

7. 11 − 3 = __8__   8. 25 + 25 = __50__

9. 40 − 12 = __28__   10. 28 + 21 = __49__

Check

11. Explain how you would use the number line to divide 49 ÷ 7.

First find 49 on the number line. Then jump back 7
spaces at a time until you reach 0. Count the number
of times you jumped back to find the quotient, 7.

IIN12   Response to Intervention • Tier 3

© Houghton Mifflin Harcourt

Do the Math

Tell students complete Problems 1–10 on student
page **IIN12**. Help them find which number they
should begin with and which direction to move.

Talk Math

• **Which number do you start at for Problem 1?** 0

• **For Problem 6, when do you stop jumping to
the left?** when you reach 0

Check

Ask: **Which number do you start at?** 49 **Which
direction do you jump?** left

© Houghton Mifflin Harcourt

Alternative Teaching Strategy

Operations with Number Lines

Objective To use number lines to practice
basic facts

Materials number cubes, ruler or straightedge

• Have students work with a partner. Draw a
number line from 0 to 40 on the board for pairs
to copy.

• Model using a number line to add, subtract,
multiply, and divide. Explain to students that
they will use number cubes to generate numbers
to solve basic facts.

• Tell one student in each group to toss the
number cube, and find that number on the
number line. Instruct the other student to toss
the cube, and add that number to the first
number. Have students record this addition fact.

• Next, tell groups to circle 12 on the number line.
Ask students to take turns tossing the number
cube, and using the number line to subtract
the number they tossed from 12. Have students
record these subtraction facts.

• To practice multiplication, direct pairs to toss
the number cube twice, and multiply the two
numbers using the number line. Tell them to
write out a multiplication sentence and share it
with the class.

• Finally, extend the number line on the board to
60, and circle 60. Instruct each pair to toss the
number cube then divide 60 by that number
using the number line. Ask: **Why do you think 60
is a good number to use for division?** Because 60
can be divided evenly by 1, 2, 3, 4, 5, and 6.

Objective
To estimate products using rounding, compatible numbers, and mental math

Vocabulary
compatible numbers Numbers that are easy to compute mentally

estimate To find a number that is close to an exact amount

product The answer to a multiplication problem

Pre-Assess

Display the following problem for students: 24 × 749. Ask: **How can you estimate the product?** round each factor and use mental math, or use compatible numbers and mental math

Invite students to choose one method to estimate the product. Have students share their answers.

Since there are several reasonable estimates, ask students to explain their estimation method and justify their result.

Rounding: 24 × 749 ➝ 20 × 700 = 14,000

Compatible numbers: 24 × 749 ➝ 20 × 750 = 15,000

Common Misconception

• Students may omit zeros when using basic facts that have zeros in their product. For example, students may record 40 × 500 as 2,000 forgetting that 4 × 5 = 20, and thus 40 × 500 = 20,000.

• To correct this, remind students to check that there are the same number of zeros in their estimate as there are in the factors <u>and</u> in the product of their basic facts. You may suggest that students record the product of the basic fact and then add zeros to it.

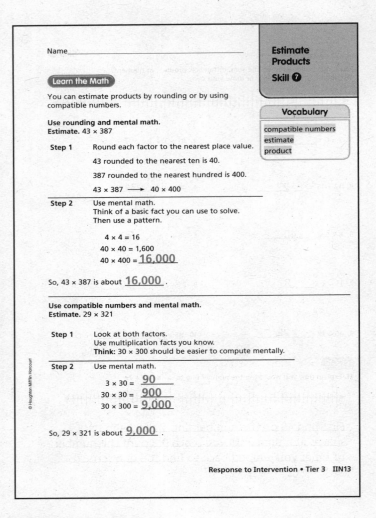

Learn the Math

Read the first problem on student page **IIN13**. Discuss each of the steps with students. Ask: **What digit will you look at to determine whether to round up or down?** the digit to the right of the rounding place Point out that they may not be rounding each factor to the same place value.

Talk Math

• **What do you notice about the number of zeros in the factors and the number of zeros in the product?** They are the same.

Direct students' attention to the second problem. Ask: **Why are 30 and 300 good numbers to use?** They are close to 29 and 321 and I can multiply them using mental math.

Use rounding to estimate the product. Show the
factors you used to estimate. Possible estimates are given.

Skill 7

1. 19 × 52
   20 × 50
   1,000

2. 37 × 64
   40 × 60
   2,400

3. 78 × 410
   80 × 400
   32,000

4. 23 × 678
   20 × 700
   14,000

5. 49 × 93
   50 × 90
   4,500

6. 55 × 625
   60 × 600
   36,000

Use compatible numbers to estimate the product. Show
the compatible numbers you used to estimate.
Possible estimates are given.

7. 22 × 249
   20 × 250
   5,000

8. 34 × 186
   30 × 180
   5,400

9. 17 × 375
   20 × 350
   7,000

10. 29 × 752
    25 × 800
    20,000

11. 39 × 147
    40 × 150
    6,000

12. 12 × 119
    12 × 120
    1,440

Check

13. Explain one way to estimate the product of 36 × 195.
    Possible answer: I can use compatible numbers. I
    know that 35 × 2 = 70, so I can use mental math
    and patterns to find that 35 × 200 = 7,000. So,
    36 × 195 is about 7,000.

IIN14   Response to Intervention • Tier 3

Do the Math

Guide students as they work through student
page IIN14. Remind students to use the steps they
have learned to estimate the products.

Talk Math

• **When might you use rounding rather than
compatible numbers?** when you cannot think of
compatible numbers that are close to the actual
factors and that are easy to multiply with
mentally

Check

Ask students to list as many basic facts as they
can that would help them estimate the product.
Guide students to see that sometimes both
rounding and compatible numbers will result in
the same estimate.

Alternative Teaching Strategy

Use Rounding to Estimate

Objective To practice rounding factors and
estimating products

Materials number cards 1–9, × sign card, index
cards

• Divide students into small groups. Provide each
group with a set of 18 blank index cards, an ×
sign card and a set of number cards 1–9. Ask
each group to record the following numbers on
separate index cards: 10, 20, 30, 40, 50, 60, 70,
80, 90, 100, 200, 300, 400, 500, 600, 700, 800,
and 900.

• Write the problem 4 × 632 on the board. Invite
students to look at their group of 18 cards. Ask:
Which card has the number closest to 632?
600 Ask students to place the number card
with the digit 4 and the × sign card to form the
multiplication problem 4 × 600.

• Remind students that they can use basic facts
and patterns to estimate products. Ask: **What
basic fact can you use to help you find 4 × 600?**
4 × 6 = 24

• Record this basic fact on the board. Ask students
to study the basic fact and the problem they
are solving. Ask: **How do you use the basic
fact to solve the problem?** The product will
be the product for the basic fact with zeros
attached. **How do you decide how many zeros
the product should have?** The product should
have the same number of zeros as there are in
the factors. **How many zeros are there in the
factors?** 4 has no zeros; 600 has two. **How many
zeros should be in the product?** two **What is
the product of 4 and 600?** 2,400

• Emphasize that this means the product of 4 and
632 is about 2,400.

• Repeat the activity with other problems. Be sure
to include a problem in which the product of
the basic fact contains a zero.

Objective
To use different strategies to multiply by 1- and 2-digit numbers

Vocabulary
factor A number that is multiplied by another number to find a product

partial products A method of multiplying in which ones, tens, hundreds, and so on are multiplied separately and then the products are added together

regroup To exchange amounts of equal value to rename a number

Pre-Assess
Write the following multiplication problems on the board:

$$\begin{array}{ccc} 20 & 425 & 19 \\ \times\ 30 & \times\ \ 3 & \times\ 12 \\ \hline 600 & 1{,}275 & 228 \end{array}$$

Have students copy each problem. Ask: **What operation will you use to solve these problems?** multiplication **What are some strategies you might use?** partial products, regrouping, basic facts and patterns

Have students work independently to solve each problem.

Common Misconception
- Students may forget to add the regrouped tens or hundreds when using the regrouping strategy to solve.

- To correct this, suggest that they use a marking system, such as placing a checkmark next to the regrouping digit as they add it, in order to remind themselves of this necessary step.

Learn the Math
Read the first problem on student page **IIN15**. Explain that the factor 17 can be broken apart as 10 and 7, and that arrays can be shaded to show the product of 6 × 10 and 6 × 7.

IIN15   Response to Intervention • Tier 3

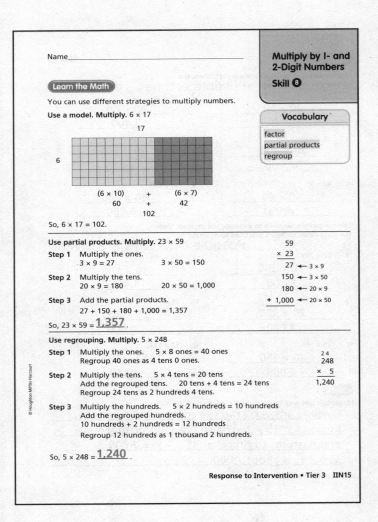

Name_____

Multiply by 1- and 2-Digit Numbers Skill 8

Learn the Math

You can use different strategies to multiply numbers.

Use a model. Multiply. 6 × 17

Vocabulary
factor
partial products
regroup

(6×10) + (6×7)
    60   +   42
            102

So, 6 × 17 = 102.

Use partial products. Multiply. 23 × 59

Step 1 Multiply the ones.
3 × 9 = 27   3 × 50 = 150

Step 2 Multiply the tens.
20 × 9 = 180   20 × 50 = 1,000

Step 3 Add the partial products.
27 + 150 + 180 + 1,000 = 1,357

So, 23 × 59 = **1,357**.

$$\begin{array}{r} 59 \\ \times\ 23 \\ \hline 27 \leftarrow 3 \times 9 \\ 150 \leftarrow 3 \times 50 \\ 180 \leftarrow 20 \times 9 \\ +\ 1{,}000 \leftarrow 20 \times 50 \end{array}$$

Use regrouping. Multiply. 5 × 248

Step 1 Multiply the ones.   5 × 8 ones = 40 ones
Regroup 40 ones as 4 tens 0 ones.

Step 2 Multiply the tens.   5 × 4 tens = 20 tens
Add the regrouped tens.   20 tens + 4 tens = 24 tens
Regroup 24 tens as 2 hundreds 4 tens.

Step 3 Multiply the hundreds.   5 × 2 hundreds = 10 hundreds
Add the regrouped hundreds.
10 hundreds + 2 hundreds = 12 hundreds
Regroup 12 hundreds as 1 thousand 2 hundreds.

So, 5 × 248 = **1,240**.

$$\begin{array}{r} 2\ 4 \\ 248 \\ \times\ \ \ 5 \\ \hline 1{,}240 \end{array}$$

Response to Intervention • Tier 3   IIN15

Ask: **How does this strategy make the problem easier to solve?** I can solve two simpler multiplication problems rather than one complex problem. Direct students' attention to the second and third problems. Discuss each strategy, step by step.

Talk Math

- **In the second Problem, how does place value help you solve multiplication problems by using partial products?** Place value tells me the value of each digit, so I know which numbers to multiply.

- **In the last problem, where do you record the 4 tens when you regroup 40 ones?** I write a zero in the ones place and I write the 4 above the tens place in 248.

- **What happens to those 4 tens?** After I find the product of 5 and the digit in the tens place, 4, I add the regrouped tens to get 24 tens.

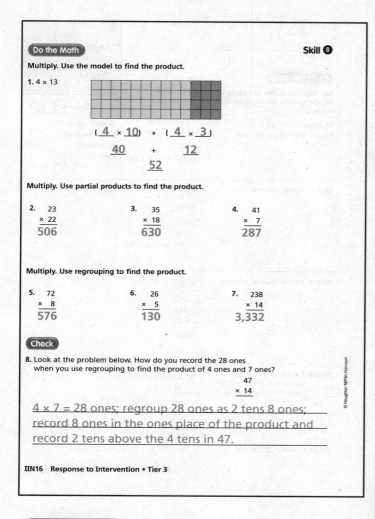

Do the Math
Skill **8**

Multiply. Use the model to find the product.

1. 4 × 13

$$(\underline{4} \times \underline{10}) + (\underline{4} \times \underline{3})$$

$$\underline{40} \quad + \quad \underline{12}$$

$$\underline{52}$$

Multiply. Use partial products to find the product.

2. 23	3. 35	4. 41
× 22	× 18	× 7
506	**630**	**287**

Multiply. Use regrouping to find the product.

5. 72	6. 26	7. 238
× 8	× 5	× 14
576	**130**	**3,332**

Check

8. Look at the problem below. How do you record the 28 ones when you use regrouping to find the product of 4 ones and 7 ones?

47
× 14

4 × 7 = 28 ones; regroup 28 ones as 2 tens 8 ones; record 8 ones in the ones place of the product and record 2 tens above the 4 tens in 47.

IIN16   Response to Intervention • Tier 3

© Houghton Mifflin Harcourt

Do the Math

Guide students through the problems on student page **IIN16**.

Talk Math

- **How do you know what the array represents?** Each smaller rectangle is a smaller multiplication problem. The sum of the 2 products equal the total product.

- **How will you use partial products to solve 22 × 23?** Find the products of 2 and 3 (6), 2 and 20 (40), 20 and 3 (60) and 20 and 20 (400). Add the partial products together: 6 + 40 + 60 + 400 = 506.

- **How do you know when to regroup when multiplying?** I regroup for any product that is greater than 9.

Check

Ask: **What happens to the 2 tens that you regroup?** After I multiply 4 by 4, I add the 2 tens to get 18 tens.

Alternative Teaching Strategy
Model Multiplication with Regrouping

Objective To use base-ten blocks to model multiplication with regrouping

Materials base-ten blocks

- Divide students into pairs. Give each pair a set of base-ten blocks.

- Write the following problem on the board: 5 × 29. Ask: **How can you use base-ten blocks to model this problem?** Show 5 groups of 29 unit cubes.

- Make the model using only ones cubes as a class. Ask: **How many ones are in each group?** 29 ones **How can you regroup the ones?** Regroup 29 ones as 2 ten and 9 ones Model regrouping with the base-ten blocks.

- Ask: **Can you regroup more ones?** yes Model regrouping the remaining ones. Ask: **How many tens do you have in all?** 14 tens **Can you regroup the tens?** Yes; 10 tens can be regrouped as 1 hundred.

- Ask: **How many hundreds, tens, and ones do you have?** 1 hundred, 4 tens, and 5 ones **What number does this represent?** 145 **What is the product of 5 and 29?** 145

- Guide students to record the multiplication problem by using numbers and symbols.

- Repeat with other multiplication problems.

© Houghton Mifflin Harcourt

Multiply Money
Skill 9

Objective
To multiply money amounts by 2-digit numbers

Vocabulary
decimal point A symbol used to separate dollars from cents in money amounts

partial product A method of multiplying in which ones, tens, hundreds, and so on are multiplied separately and then the products are added together

place value The value of a digit in a number, based on the location of the digit

regroup To exchange amounts of equal value to rename a number

Pre-Assess
Write the following money multiplication problems on the board:

$1.43	$2.27	$3.89
× 36	× 42	× 23
$51.48	$95.34	$89.47

Have students copy each problem. Ask: **What operation will you use to solve these problems?** multiplication **What are some strategies you might use?** Possible answers: regrouping, partial products **How should you record your answer?** I will write the answer in dollars and cents.

Ask students to work independently to find each product.

Common Misconception
- Students may incorrectly place the decimal point and dollar sign.

- To correct this, remind students to place the decimal point two places to the left to show cents and the dollar sign on the left to show dollars.

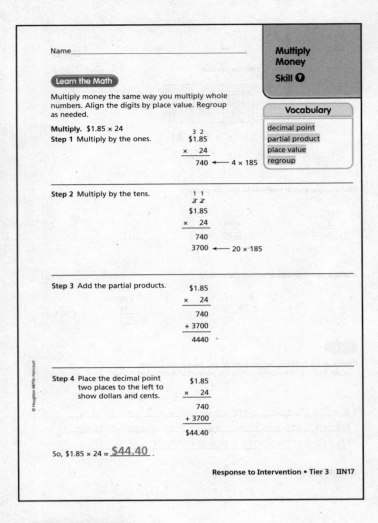

Learn the Math
Read the problem on student page **IIN17**. Emphasize to students that multiplying with money is just like multiplying with whole numbers. Guide students through the steps to multiply the ones and record the partial product.

Guide students through the steps to multiply the tens and record the partial product. Ask students to add the partial products, pointing out that the dollar sign and decimal point must be written in the answer.

Talk Math
- **In what order do you multiply the digits?** First I multiply the ones, then the tens, then the hundreds.

- **What happens to the regrouped number that you record above the first factor?** It is added to the product of the next place value.

Do the Math

Find the product. Show your work.

1.
$$\begin{array}{r} \$1.55 \\ \times\ 18 \\ \hline 1240 \\ +\ 1550 \\ \hline \$27.90 \end{array}$$

2.
$$\begin{array}{r} \$4.37 \\ \times\ 46 \\ \hline 2622 \\ +\ 17480 \\ \hline \$201.02 \end{array}$$

3.
$$\begin{array}{r} \$5.73 \\ \times\ 26 \\ \hline 3438 \\ +\ 11460 \\ \hline \$148.98 \end{array}$$

4.
$$\begin{array}{r} \$2.28 \\ \times\ 49 \\ \hline 2052 \\ +\ 9120 \\ \hline \$111.72 \end{array}$$

5.
$$\begin{array}{r} \$6.40 \\ \times\ 25 \\ \hline 3200 \\ +\ 12800 \\ \hline \$160.00 \end{array}$$

6.
$$\begin{array}{r} \$3.99 \\ \times\ 52 \\ \hline 798 \\ +\ 19950 \\ \hline \$207.48 \end{array}$$

7.
$$\begin{array}{r} \$4.62 \\ \times\ 35 \\ \hline 2310 \\ +\ 13860 \\ \hline \$161.70 \end{array}$$

8.
$$\begin{array}{r} \$2.84 \\ \times\ 70 \\ \hline 0 \\ +\ 19880 \\ \hline \$198.80 \end{array}$$

9.
$$\begin{array}{r} \$7.49 \\ \times\ 22 \\ \hline 1498 \\ +\ 14980 \\ \hline \$164.78 \end{array}$$

10.
$$\begin{array}{r} \$9.95 \\ \times\ 17 \\ \hline 6965 \\ +\ 9950 \\ \hline \$169.15 \end{array}$$

Check

11. Explain how you know where to put the decimal point in a multiplication problem with money. What other symbol do you need to use? Why?

Possible response: I place the decimal point 2 places from the right to separate dollars from cents. I place the dollar sign on the left to show that it is a money amount.

© Houghton Mifflin Harcourt

Do the Math

Guide students through the problems on student page **IIN18**.

Talk Math

• **What do you do after you find the product of the ones and the product of the tens?** I add the partial products together.

• **How do you know when to regroup when multiplying?** I regroup for any two numbers whose product is greater than 9.

• **How can you check that your answer is reasonable?** I can estimate by rounding numbers and using mental math. Then I can compare my answer and the estimate to see if my answer is close.

Check

Ask: **How do you show that a number is a money amount?** I use a dollar sign and a decimal.

Alternative Teaching Strategy

Model Multiplication with Money

Objective To model multiplication with money

Materials play money

• Divide students into pairs. Give each pair play money.

• Write the following problem on the board:

$$\begin{array}{r} \$1.50 \\ \times\ 12 \\ \hline \end{array}$$

Ask: **How can you use money to model this problem?** Possible answer: Show 12 groups of 1 dollar and 50 cents each.

• Instruct students to work through the problem first by multiplying the money amount by the ones digit, 2. Ask: **What is the value of two groups of 1 dollar and 50 cents?** 3 dollars or $3.00 Show students how to record the multiplication with regrouping. Ask students to follow along by writing the process on their papers.

• Repeat the procedure by multiplying the money amount by the tens digit. Ask: **By how many tens do you multiply 1 dollar and 50 cents?** 1 ten **What is the value of ten groups of 1 dollar and 50 cents?** 15 dollars or $15.00 Again, show students how to record the multiplication. Ask students to follow along by writing the process.

• Guide students to add $3.00 and $15.00 to find the total. Ask: **What is the total value?** $18.00 Demonstrate how to record the dollar sign and decimal point in the answer. Say: **So, 1 dollar and 50 cents multiplied by 12 is $18.00.**

• Repeat with other examples.

Estimate Quotients
Skill ⑩

Objective
To estimate quotients using rounding, compatible numbers, and mental math

Vocabulary
compatible numbers Numbers that are easy to compute mentally

dividend The number that is to be divided in a division problem

estimate To find a number that is close to an exact amount

round To replace a number with another number that tells about how many or how much

Pre-Assess
Display the following problem for students: 1,592 ÷ 4. Ask: **Which number is the dividend?** 1,592 **Which number is the divisor?** 4 **How can you estimate the quotient?** Round to the nearest thousand and use mental math to solve. **Is there another way to find the estimate?** Use compatible numbers and mental math to solve.

Invite students to use both methods to estimate the quotient. Since there are several reasonable estimates, ask students to justify their answers.
Rounding: 1,592 ÷ 4 → 2,000 ÷ 4 = 500
Compatible numbers: 1,592 ÷ 4 → 1,600 ÷ 4 = 400

Common Misconception
- Students may suggest estimates that are not reasonable simply because they are rounding incorrectly.

- To correct this, review rounding rules. Remind students to look at the digit to the right of the rounding place. If the digit is equal to or greater than 5, the digit in the rounding place is increased by 1. If it is less than 5, it stays the same. All of the digits to the right of the digit in the rounding place are replaced with zeros.

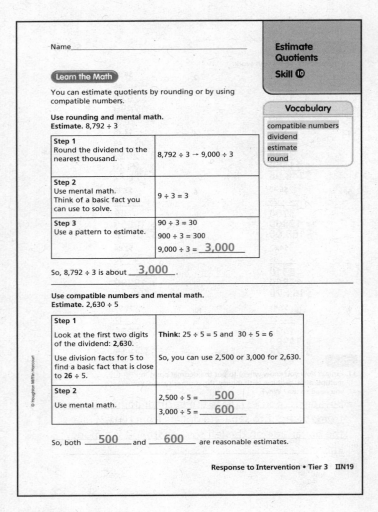

Learn the Math
Read the first problem on student page **IIN19**. Discuss each of the three steps with students.

Talk Math
- **What digit will you look at to determine whether to increase the digit in the thousands place?** the digit in the hundreds place

- **What pattern do you see in Step 3?** For each extra zero in the dividend, there is an extra zero in the quotient.

- **Why do you use division facts for 5 in the second problem?** The divisor is 5, so I am looking for a number into which 5 divides evenly.

- **Why can you use either 2,500 or 3,000 as a compatible number?** They are both close to 2,630.

Do the Math

Skill ⑩

Estimate the quotient. Use rounding and mental math.

Possible estimate are given.

1. 4,115 ÷ 8

500

2. 1,945 ÷ 2

1,000

3. 986 ÷ 5

200

4. 5,881 ÷ 3

2,000

5. 2,186 ÷ 2

1,000

6. 6,881 ÷ 7

1,000

Estimate the quotient. Use compatible numbers and mental math.

Possible estimate are given.

7. 245 ÷ 6

40

8. 2,139 ÷ 3

700

9. 1,742 ÷ 6

300

10. 637 ÷ 8

80

11. 4,312 ÷ 6

700

12. 297 ÷ 7

40

Check

13. Why is rounding to the nearest thousand NOT a good method for estimating the quotient for 1,396 ÷ 7?

1,396 rounded to the nearest thousand is 1,000.
7 does not divide evenly into 1,000, so you cannot
use mental math to find the estimate.

Do the Math

Help students work through the problems on student page **IIN20**. For Problems 1–6, remind students to round to the greatest place value in the dividend. For Problems 7–12, encourage students to choose compatible numbers that are basic math facts.

Talk Math

- **In Problem 2, would the exact answer be more or less than the estimate?** less

- **How do you know?** I rounded up, so the estimate is higher than the actual quotient.

Check

Ask: **How could you use compatible numbers to solve the problem?** 1,396 is close to 1,400; 14 ÷ 7 = 2, so 1,400 ÷ 7 = 200.

Alternative Teaching Strategy

Use Compatible Numbers to Estimate

Objective To practice using compatible numbers to estimate quotients

Materials number cards 2–9

- Prepare a list of 3- and 4-digit dividends such as 195; 809; 2,160; 3,619; 4,278; 5,477; 7,314. On the ledge of the board or on a similar surface, display the number cards 2–9.

- Write one of the dividends from the list, such as 2,160, on the board and select a number card such as 2. Record the resulting problem (2,160 ÷ 2) on the board. Ask: **What basic fact would you use to solve this problem?** 2 ÷ 2 = 1 **What compatible number would you use?** 2,000 **What is the estimated quotient?** 1,000 Record this problem on the board: 2,000 ÷ 2 = 1,000.

- Invite a student to the board to match a different number card to the same dividend and state the new problem. For example, a student may select 3 and write 2,160 ÷ 3. Ask: **What basic fact would you use to solve this problem?** Possible response: 21 ÷ 3 = 7 Have students work in pairs to write the problem with a compatible number and find the estimated quotient. 2,100 ÷ 3 = 700

- Continue inviting students to match number cards to 2,160, identify a basic fact, and find an estimated quotient. When all of the number card-dividend pairs have been matched, display the full set of number cards again, write a new dividend from the list on the board, and repeat the activity. Note that not every number card-dividend pair will result in a problem for which there is an easily identifiable basic fact. (For example, 3 and 4,278.) Challenge students to match and solve as many number card-dividend pairs as possible.

Objective

To place the first digit in a quotient by using an estimate or place value

Pre-Assess

Display the following problems. Ask students to estimate the quotients using compatible numbers.

1. $3\overline{)137}$ $\overset{40}{3\overline{)120}}$ or $\overset{50}{3\overline{)150}}$

2. $5\overline{)462}$ $\overset{90}{5\overline{)450}}$ or $\overset{100}{5\overline{)500}}$

3. $7\overline{)189}$ $\overset{20}{7\overline{)140}}$ or $\overset{30}{7\overline{)210}}$

Display the second set of problems. Ask students to use place value to tell where they would place the first digit of the quotient.

4. $6\overline{)756}$ hundreds place

5. $3\overline{)198}$ tens place

6. $8\overline{)644}$ tens place

Common Misconception

- Students may determine the correct place for the first digit of the quotient, but record the digit in the incorrect place.

- To correct this, suggest to students that they mark an X in the hundreds place of the quotient if the first digit of the quotient belongs in the tens place.

Learn the Math

Read the first problem on student page **IIN21**. Review the steps for estimating the quotient. Ask: **How do you determine which compatible numbers to use?** Since the divisor is 4, I use division facts for 4. I think of a basic fact that is close to the number shown by the first two digits in the number I am dividing. Review the steps for

---

Learn the Math

You can use an estimate or place value to place the first digit in the quotient.

Use compatible numbers to estimate to place the first digit in the quotient.

Divide 172 by 4. Write $4\overline{)172}$.

Step 1	Step 2	Step 3
Use compatible numbers to estimate. Think: $4\overline{)160}$ or $4\overline{)200}$ $\overset{\blacksquare}{4\overline{)172}}$ So, the first digit is in the tens place.	Divide the 17 tens. $\begin{array}{r} 4 \\ 4\overline{)172} \\ -16 \\ \hline 1 \end{array}$ Divide. $4\overline{)17}$ Multiply. $4 \times 4 = 16$ Subtract. $17 - 16 = 1$ Compare. $1 < 4$	Bring down the 2 ones. Divide the 12 ones. $\begin{array}{r} 43 \\ 4\overline{)172} \\ -16\downarrow \\ \hline 12 \\ -12 \\ \hline 0 \end{array}$ Divide. $4\overline{)12}$ Multiply. $4 \times 3 = 12$ Subtract. $12 - 12 = 0$ Compare. $0 < 4$

So, 172 divided by 4 is __43__.

Use place value to place the first digit in the quotient.

Divide 380 by 5. Write $5\overline{)380}$.

Step 1	Step 2	Step 3
Look at the hundreds. $5\overline{)380}$ $3 < 5$ You cannot divide 5 into 3, so look at the tens. $5\overline{)380}$ $38 > 5$ Place the first digit in the tens place.	Divide the 38 tens. $\begin{array}{r} 7 \\ 5\overline{)380} \\ -35 \\ \hline 3 \end{array}$ Divide. $5\overline{)38}$ Multiply. $5 \times 7 = 35$ Subtract. $38 - 35 = 3$ Compare. $3 < 5$	Bring down the 0 ones. Divide the 30 ones. $\begin{array}{r} 76 \\ 5\overline{)380} \\ -35\downarrow \\ \hline 30 \\ -30 \\ \hline 0 \end{array}$ Divide. $5\overline{)30}$ Multiply. $5 \times 6 = 30$ Subtract. $30 - 30 = 0$ Compare. $0 < 5$

So, 380 divided by 5 is __76__.

division: divide, multiply, subtract, and compare. Ask: **Why must the difference be less than the divisor?** If it is not less than the divisor, then you could divide again.

Direct students' attention to the second problem. Explain the process for using place value to place the first digit in the quotient.

Talk Math

- **Why do you look at the hundreds place first?** If the digit in the hundreds place is equal to or larger than the divisor, I can divide the hundreds.

- **Can you divide 3 hundreds by 5 in the second problem?** No, I need to look at the tens place.

Walk students through the steps to complete the division.

Do the Math

Tell where to place the first digit. Then divide.

1. 2)438 $\underline{219}$ _hundreds_ place   2. 9)918 $\underline{102}$ _hundreds_ place

3. 5)105 $\underline{21}$ _tens_ place   4. 7)574 $\underline{82}$ _tens_ place

5. 4)956 $\underline{239}$ _hundreds_ place   6. 9)315 $\underline{35}$ _tens_ place

7. 5)825 $\underline{165}$ _hundreds_ place   8. 8)896 $\underline{112}$ _hundreds_ place

Check

9. Look at Problem 7. Where would you place the first digit if the dividend were 225 instead of 825? Explain.

Possible explanation: If the dividend were 225 instead of 825, the first digit would go in the tens place. Because 2 < 5, you would begin division with 22 tens.

Do the Math

Direct students to follow the division steps they have learned to complete the problems on student page IIN22.

Talk Math

• **In Problem 1, what method will you use to determine where to place the first digit?** Answers will vary. Invite students to share their ideas. Ask them to explain their reasoning.

Check

Guide students to explain what would change if the dividend were 225 instead of 825. Ask: **How does the divisor, 5, compare with the first digit in the dividend 825?** 8 is greater than 5, so you can divide hundreds. **How does the first digit in 225 compare?** 2 is less than 5, so you *cannot* place the first digit in the hundreds place.

Alternative Teaching Strategy

Practice and Compare Strategies

Objective To practice and compare *use an estimate* and *use place value* as strategies for placing the first digit in the quotient

Materials index cards with division problems, labeled on the back with either *use an estimate* or *use place value*

• Review the two strategies for placing the first digit in the quotient. Write the following problems on the board: 4)300; 3)519.

• Ask: **In the first problem, if you use estimation to place the first digit, what compatible number would you use?** 280 or 320 **What are the quotients for 280 divided by 4 and 320 divided by 4?** 70; 80 **What do those quotients tell you about where to place the first digit?** Both of the estimates have the first digit in the tens place, so I place the first digit of the quotient in the tens place.

• Ask: **In the second problem, if you use place value to place the first digit, what numbers do you compare?** the divisor, 3, and the first digit of the dividend, 5 **In which place do you write the first digit of the quotient?** hundreds **How do you know?** 5 > 3, so 5 can be divided by 3.

• Give pairs of students an index card. Direct students to place the first digit in the quotient by using the strategy written on the back of the card.

• Invite students to share their work with the class. Ask them to explain how they used the strategy.

• Facilitate a class discussion comparing the two strategies. Ask: **What advantage is there to using place value to place the first digit?** Possible response: Place value is a quick way to place the first digit, especially when the divisor is less than the first digit of the dividend. **What advantage is there to using an estimate to place the first digit?** Possible response: You can use the estimate to check if the answer is reasonable.

Factors
Skill ⑫

Objective
To find factors using arrays

Materials
square tiles, grid paper

Vocabulary
array An arrangement of objects in rows and columns

factor A number that is multiplied by another number to find a product

Pre-Assess
Draw the following arrays on the board:

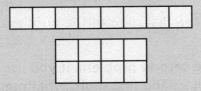

Ask students to use the arrays to write multiplication sentences.

Ask: **How are these arrays similar?** They both have 8 tiles in all. **How are they different?** The first has 1 row of 8 and the second has 2 rows of 4.

Ask students to use these arrays to list all of the factors of 8. 1, 2, 4, 8

Common Misconception

• Students may forget to list 1 and the number itself as factors of a number.

• To correct this, remind students that *every* whole number has 1 and itself as a factor. Suggest that they model this array and record its factors before moving on to other arrays.

Learn the Math

Read through the introductory text on student page IIN23. Guide students to see that each set of factors—1 and 9, 9 and 1, and 3 and 3—yields the same product, 9. Point out that when an array forms a square, there is only 1 factor.

IIN23   Response to Intervention • Tier 3

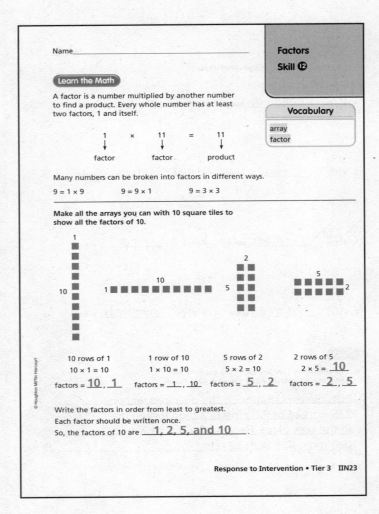

Direct students' attention to the problem. Ask: **How many rows are in the first array?** 10 **How many columns are in the first array?** 1 Say: **So, 10 and 1 are factors of 10.**

Direct students' attention to the second array. Ask: **How many rows are there?** 1 **How many columns are there?** 10 **What are the factors?** 1, 10

Ask similar questions for the last two arrays.

Talk Math

• **How do you know when you have found all of the factors of a number?** I have found all of the factors when I cannot make any new arrays.

• **What are all the factors of 10?** 1, 2, 5, and 10

© Houghton Mifflin Harcourt

Do the Math

Skill ⑫

Use arrays to find all of the factors of each product.

1. 12

   Factors = 1, 2, 3, 4, 6, 12

2. 30

   Factors = 1, 2, 3, 5, 6, 10, 15, 30

3. 24

   Factors = 1, 2, 3, 4, 6, 8, 12, 24

4. 18

   Factors = 1, 2, 3, 6, 9, 18

5. 40

   Factors = 1, 2, 4, 5, 8, 10, 20, 40

6. 10

   Factors = 1, 2, 5, 10

7. 36

   Factors = 1, 2, 3, 4, 6, 9, 12, 18, 36

8. 21

   Factors = 1, 3, 7, 21

9. 44

   Factors = 1, 2, 4, 11, 22, 44

10. 41

    Factors = 1, 41

Check

11. Explain how you can use arrays to find the factors of a number.

    The number of rows in the array is one factor and the number of columns in the array is the other factor. Once I have made all the arrays for a number, I can list the numbers of rows and the number of columns to show all the different factors.

© Houghton Mifflin Harcourt

Do the Math

Guide students through the problems on student page **IIN24**. If needed, students can use square tiles to make arrays. Then ask students to list the factors.

Talk Math

- **How do you know what the factors of a number are?** The factors are modeled by the arrays.

- **In Problem 10, why are there only two factors?** because 41 has only two factors, one and itself

Check

Ask students to discuss what they know about arrays. Guide them to conclude that arrays are visual representations of the factors of a number.

© Houghton Mifflin Harcourt

Alternative Teaching Strategy

Find Factors with a Multiplication Table

Objective To use a multiplication table to find factors

Materials multiplication table (12 by 12), square tiles

- Ask students to work in pairs. Give each pair a multiplication table and some square tiles.

- Ask: **How can you use the multiplication table to find 2 × 6?** Find the box at which the row for 2 and the column for 6 meet. The number in this box is the product. **What is the product?** 12

- Have students study the multiplication table. Ask: **Is 12 found anywhere else on the table?** Possible response: Yes, at the intersection of row 3, column 4. **What does this tell you about the factors of 12?** 3 and 4 are also factors of 12

- Ask students to discuss how they might use the multiplication table to find all of the factors of 12. As students share their ideas, guide them to conclude that to find the factors of any number on the multiplication table, they should find each place that the number is listed on the table and then look across the row and up the column to find the factors.

- Invite students to try this method to find the factors of 36. 3, 4, 6, 9, 12 Ask: **Are these all of the factors of 36?** no **Why aren't all of the factors listed in the table?** The table just shows multiplication facts from 1 through 12.

- Ask: **What other method might you use to find the remaining factors?** arrays Ask students to use arrays to identify the remaining factors. 1, 2, 18, 36

- Help students evaluate what they have learned. Ask: **When is using the multiplication table to find factors most helpful?** when the product has factors that are all less than or equal to 12 **When is it not so helpful?** when the product has factors that are greater than 12

Common Factors
Skill ⑬

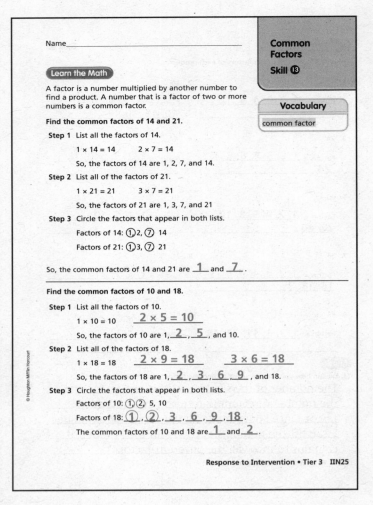

Objective
To identify common factors for pairs of numbers

Vocabulary
common factor A number that is a factor of two or more numbers

Pre-Assess
Write 12 and 24 on the board, and ask students to identify all common factors. 1, 2, 3, 4, 6, 12

Common Misconception

- Students may not list all the factors of a number before looking for common factors.

- To correct this, tell students to write the factors for a number in pairs. For 15, pairs of factors are 1 and 15, 3 and 5. Students should write numbers in pairs and exclude the repeating factors.

Learn the Math

Have students look at student page **IIN25**. Review the meaning of *factor*. Remind students that every number has at least two factors: 1 and the number itself. Review the process of finding factors.

Tell students that identifying common factors for two or more numbers involves finding all factors for each number first. Stress that *all* factors must be listed. Direct students to write the common factors of 14 and 21 based on the circled numbers in the list.

Help students understand that since 1 is a factor for every number, it is a common factor for every pair of numbers.

Guide students to recognize that 2 is a factor for all even numbers because all even numbers are divisible by 2. Therefore, all even numbers have at least 1 and 2 as common factors.

Talk Math

- **Which number is a common factor for all pairs of numbers?** 1

- **Which numbers are common factors for any pair of even numbers?** 1 and 2

- **Why is 2 not a common factor for 14 and 21?** 2 is not a factor for 21 because 21 is odd.

Do the Math

Skill ⑬

List all the factors for each pair of numbers. Then identify the common factors.

1. 3, 17
Factors of 3: 1, 3
Factors of 17: 1, 17
Common Factors: 1

2. 12, 16
Factors of 12: 1, 2, 3, 4, 6, 12
Factors of 16: 1, 2, 4, 8, 16
Common Factors: 1, 2, 4

3. 15, 25
Factors of 15: 1, 3, 5, 15
Factors of 25: 1, 5, 25
Common Factors: 1, 5

4. 10, 100
Factors of 10: 1, 2, 5, 10
Factors of 100: 1, 2, 4, 5, 10, 20, 25, 50, 100
Common Factors: 1, 2, 5, 10

5. 28, 49
Factors of 28: 1, 2, 4, 7, 14, 28
Factors of 49: 1, 7, 49
Common Factors: 1, 7

6. 11, 44
Factors of 11: 1, 11
Factors of 44: 1, 2, 4, 11, 22, 44
Common Factors: 1, 11

7. 12, 20
Factors of 12: 1, 2, 3, 4, 6, 12
Factors of 20: 1, 2, 4, 5, 10, 20
Common Factors: 1, 2, 4

8. 16, 27
Factors of 16: 1, 2, 4, 8, 16
Factors of 27: 1, 3, 9, 27
Common Factors: 1

Check

9. Chris says the common factors for 14 and 28 are 1, 2, and 7. Are these all the common factors? If not, what is missing?

No, 14 is missing.

Do the Math

Have students look at student page **IIN26**. Review the steps of finding common factors. Ask students to say whether the numbers in a problem are both odd, both even, or odd and even. Remind students to find *every* factor for each number before identifying common factors.

Talk Math

- **How can you be sure you have found all factors for a number?** I write them in pairs, and stop when I list a factor more than once.

- **Can 2 be a common factor for 28 and 49?** no

- **For Problem 3, why are there only 3 factors of 25?** Because you would not list 5 twice for the fact 5 × 5

Check

Guide students to see that one of the numbers in a pair may be a common factor for the pair. 14 is a factor for both 14 and for 28.

Alternative Teaching Strategy

Use Arrays to Find Common Factors

Objective To identify common factors of numbers

Materials grid paper or tiles

- Place students in groups of three. Write the following pairs of numbers on the board: 16, 18; 12, 24; 27, 33.

- Explain to students that they will make as many arrays as possible for each number. Direct them to use grid paper or tiles to make arrays for each number. Explain that the number of squares in each row or column of an array is a factor of the number.

- Instruct one student from each group to make all the arrays for the first number in a pair. Ask the second students of each group to make all the arrays for the second number. Direct the third student to list all the factors found in the arrays and identify the common factors. Tell students to switch roles after finishing a pair, until every student has had a chance to find common factors. The activity can be repeated with different pairs of numbers.

- Have groups share their results with the class. Check the work together, making sure that each group has made all the possible arrays and found all factors for each number.

- The factors for these sets of numbers are listed below. The common factors are circled.

  1. 16: ①, ②, 4, 8, 16
     18: ①, ②, 3, 6, 9, 18

  2. 12: ①, ②, ③, ④, ⑥, ⑫
     24: ①, ②, ③, ④, ⑥, 8, ⑫, 24

  3. 27: ①, ③, 9, 27
     33: ①, ③, 11, 33

Objective
To find multiples by making a model, skip-counting, and making a list

Materials
counters, number lines

Vocabulary
multiple The product of two whole numbers is called a multiple of each of those numbers

skip-count A pattern for counting forward or backward

Pre-Assess
Write the following patterns on the board:

4: 4, 8, 12, 16, 20, _24_ , _28_ , _32_
5: 5, 10, 15, 20, 25, _30_ , _35_ , _40_
6: 6, 12, 18, 24, 36, _42_ , _48_ , _54_

Ask students to find the missing multiples in each pattern. Ask: **How can you describe the numbers in the first pattern?** Each number is 4 more than the one before it. **How can you describe the numbers in the second and third patterns?** The second has numbers that are multiples of 5; the third has numbers that are multiples of 6.

Common Misconception

• Students may forget that each number has itself as a multiple.

• To correct this, remind students that the product of 1 and any number is that number. Since a multiple of a number is defined as any product of that number and another whole number, each whole number always has itself as a multiple.

Learn the Math

Read through the introductory text on student page IIN27.

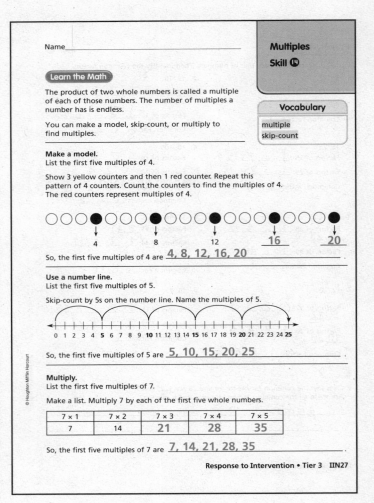

Learn the Math

The product of two whole numbers is called a multiple of each of those numbers. The number of multiples a number has is endless.

You can make a model, skip-count, or multiply to find multiples.

Vocabulary
multiple
skip-count

Make a model.
List the first five multiples of 4.

Show 3 yellow counters and then 1 red counter. Repeat this pattern of 4 counters. Count the counters to find the multiples of 4. The red counters represent multiples of 4.

So, the first five multiples of 4 are _4, 8, 12, 16, 20_

Use a number line.
List the first five multiples of 5.

Skip-count by 5s on the number line. Name the multiples of 5.

So, the first five multiples of 5 are _5, 10, 15, 20, 25_

Multiply.
List the first five multiples of 7.

Make a list. Multiply 7 by each of the first five whole numbers.

7 × 1	7 × 2	7 × 3	7 × 4	7 × 5
7	14	21	28	35

So, the first five multiples of 7 are _7, 14, 21, 28, 35_

Response to Intervention • Tier 3 IIN27

Discuss each method of finding multiples. Ask: **How can you find the sixth multiple of 4?** Add 3 yellow counters and 1 red counter; count up to the last red counter. **What is the sixth multiple of 4?** 24 Challenge students to find the sixth and seventh multiples of 5 and 7 in the last two problems, and to explain their reasoning.

Talk Math

• **How many multiples does each number have?** The amount is endless—each time you multiply by a whole number, the product is a multiple.

• **Which method do you like best? Why?** Possible answer: Skip-counting; I can check the number line to see that I am jumping the correct number of spaces to find each multiple.

Do the Math

Skill 🄬

List the first twelve multiples of each number.

1. 3

Multiples = 3, 6, 9, 12, 15, 18, 21, 24, 27, 30, 33, 36

2. 6

Multiples = 6, 12, 18, 24, 30, 36, 42, 48, 54, 60, 66, 72

3. 2

Multiples = 2, 4, 6, 8, 10, 12, 14, 16, 18, 20, 22, 24

4. 11

Multiples = 11, 22, 33, 44, 55, 66, 77, 88, 99, 110, 121, 132

5. 10

Multiples = 10, 20, 30, 40, 50, 60, 70, 80, 90, 100, 110, 120

6. 8

Multiples = 8, 16, 24, 32, 40, 48, 56, 64, 72, 80, 88, 96

7. 9

Multiples = 9, 18, 27, 36, 45, 54, 63, 72, 81, 90, 99, 108

8. 1

Multiples = 1, 2, 3, 4, 5, 6, 7, 8, 9, 10, 11, 12

Check

9. Tell whether 24 is a multiple of each number below. How do you know?
1, 2, 3, 4, 5, 6, 7, 8, 9, 10, 11, 12

24 is a multiple of 1, 2, 3, 4, 6, 8, and 12. Possible response: I listed the multiplication facts that have 24 as a product: $1 \times 24 = 24$, $2 \times 12 = 24$, $3 \times 8 = 24$, $4 \times 6 = 24$, $6 \times 4 = 24$, $8 \times 3 = 24$, $12 \times 2 = 24$.

Do the Math

Guide students through the problems on student page **IIN28**. Provide students with counters and number lines, and invite them to use the method they prefer to identify the multiples of a number.

Talk Math

• **What is the relationship between the numbers 5 and 10? Use the word *multiple* to explain.** 10 is a multiple of 5.

• **How are the numbers 5 and 10 related to 30? Use the word *multiple* to explain.** 30 is a multiple of 5 ($5 \times 6 = 30$) and a multiple of 10 ($10 \times 3 = 30$).

Check

Ask: **Is 24 a multiple of 5? How do you know?** No, there is not a whole number which I can multiply 5 by to get 24. The two closest products are 20 (5×4) and 25 (5×5).

Alternative Teaching Strategy

Find Multiples on a Multiplication Table

Objective To use a multiplication table to identify multiples

Materials multiplication table (12 by 12)

• Distribute multiplication tables to pairs of students.

• Write *8* on the board. Ask: **Where is one place you see 8 in the table (not in the rows and columns labels)?** 8 is in the square where the row for 2 and the column for 4 intersect. Have students place their finger on the number.

• Ask: **What does it mean to find 8 in row 2 and column 4?** It means that $2 \times 4 = 8$ Guide students to see that 8 is a multiple of both 2 and 4.

• Ask: **How can you use the multiplication table to find other multiples of 2?** Look at row 2. Each number in this row is a multiple of 2. **Call out various numbers and ask students to raise their hands if the numbers are multiples of 2. If the number is a multiple of 2, ask them to identify what number multiplied by 2 will have that multiple as a product. For example, say: Is 3 a multiple of 2?** no **Is 4 a multiple of 2?** yes **What times 2 is 4?** 2

• Next, ask: **Where else on the table can you find multiples of 2?** Look at column 2. Each number in this column is a multiple of 2. **Instruct students to compare these numbers with the numbers in row 2. Students should recognize that the same numbers are listed vertically and horizontally.**

• Invite pairs to take turns asking classmates questions about multiples that can be answered using the table. For example, a student may ask, *Is 35 a multiple of 7?* yes *What are two numbers that have 18 as a multiple?* Possible response: 3 and 9

• The student who answers the question correctly asks the next question. Continue the activity until everyone has had a chance to ask and answer a question.

Understand Fractions
Skill ⓖ

Objective
To read and write fractions

Materials
fraction bars, fraction circles

Vocabulary
denominator The number below the bar in a fraction that tells how many equal parts are in the whole

fraction A number that names a part of a whole or a part of a group

numerator The number above the bar in a fraction that tells how many equal parts of the whole are being considered

unit fraction A fraction with a numerator of 1

Pre-Assess
Display the following pictures. Ask students to write a fraction for each shaded part.

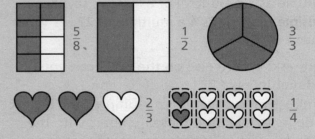

Common Misconception
- Students may have difficulty with fractions that name part of a group.
- To help students, remind them that naming part of a group requires the same steps as naming part of a whole:
  (1) Identify the number of equal parts. Write this as the denominator.
  (2) Identify the number of parts being considered. Write this as the numerator.

Learn the Math

Have students use fraction bars to model the first two examples on student page **IIN29**.

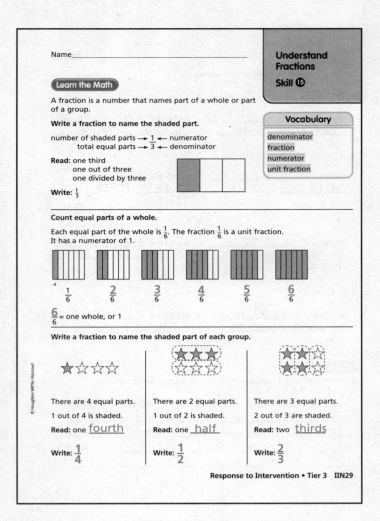

With students' models in front of them, discuss the meaning of fractions. Identify the different ways to read a fraction, and explain that "one third" means "one of three equal parts," "one sixth" means "one of six equal parts," and so on. Discuss writing fractions that name a whole, emphasizing the definition of a unit fraction. Ask: **How do you know that 6 sixths names one whole?** Six out of six equal parts are shaded; the whole is shaded.

Next, discuss fractions that name part of a group. Ask: **Do you need to know the number of objects in each group?** No, I need to know the number of equal groups and how many of those groups are shaded.

Talk Math

- **What does a 5 as the numerator tell you?** There are 5 equal parts being considered.

- **What does an 8 as the denominator tell you?** The total number of equal parts is 8.

Do the Math

Skill **15**

Write a fraction for the shaded part. Write a fraction for the unshaded part.

1. $\dfrac{1}{4}$; $\dfrac{3}{4}$

2. $\dfrac{3}{8}$; $\dfrac{5}{8}$

3. $\dfrac{3}{4}$; $\dfrac{1}{4}$

4. $\dfrac{1}{6}$; $\dfrac{5}{6}$

Shade the picture to show the fraction. Arrangements may vary.

5. $\dfrac{2}{5}$

6. $\dfrac{4}{9}$

7. $\dfrac{3}{3}$

8. $\dfrac{1}{2}$

Write the fraction for each.

9. seven out of nine ___ $\dfrac{7}{9}$

10. four divided by five ___ $\dfrac{4}{5}$

11. three sixths ___ $\dfrac{3}{6}$

12. one eighth ___ $\dfrac{1}{8}$

Check

13. Zara drew some triangles on the board. She shaded 7 of the triangles, and left the last 4 triangles unshaded. She says that $\frac{4}{7}$ of the triangles are unshaded. Do you agree? Explain?

I disagree. If 7 are shaded and 4 are unshaded, there are a total of 11 triangles. 4 out of 11 triangles is $\frac{4}{11}$.

IIN30   Response to Intervention • Tier 3

Do the Math

Guide students through the problems on student page IIN30. Read each direction line aloud and check that students understand what they are being asked to find before they begin.

Talk Math

• **What is another way to say two thirds?** Possible answers: two out of three, two divided by three

• **If $\frac{2}{8}$ of a whole is shaded, how many more parts need to be shaded to shade the whole? Explain.** 6 parts, because 8 out of 8 is 1 whole.

Check

Suggest that students use simpler numbers. Ask: **If there was 1 shaded triangle and 1 unshaded triangle, what would be the fraction of unshaded triangles?** $\frac{1}{2}$

Alternative Teaching Strategy
Model Fractions

Objective To model, read, and write fractions

Materials construction paper, two-color counters

• Ask students to work in small groups. Provide each group with several sheets of construction paper and a set of counters.

• Direct students to fold a sheet of paper in half and then open it. Ask: **How many equal parts are there?** 2 Have students shade one part. **How many parts are shaded?** 1 **What fraction does your paper model?** one half

• Next, have students draw two circles. Direct students to place two red counters in one circle and two yellow counters in the other circle. **How many equal parts are there in the model?** 2 **How many parts are red?** 1 **What fraction of the group is red?** one half

• Ask students to discuss the way one half is represented in each model. Then invite a student to the board to write the fraction. Ask: **What does the 1 represent?** 1 part of the whole or group; the part that is being considered **What does the 2 represent?** the number of equal parts the whole or group is divided into

• Ask: **How can you use a sheet of paper to model one third?** Fold the paper into three equal parts, and shade one part. **How can you use counters to model one third?** Possible answer: Make three groups of two counters. Place red counters in one group and yellow counters in two groups. Have students complete the models and write the fraction the red counters represent. one third, $\frac{1}{3}$

• Continue asking students to make fraction models with paper and counters. Invite students to share and discuss each model they make. Be sure to include models of fractions that are not unit fractions and models of fractions that name a whole.

Response to Intervention • Tier 3   IIN30

Compare Fractions
Skill 16

Objective
To compare fractions with like and unlike denominators

Materials
two-color counters, fraction bars, number lines

Vocabulary
denominator The number below the bar in a fraction that tells how many equal parts are in the whole

greater than (>) A symbol used to compare two numbers with the greater number given first

less than (<) A symbol used to compare two numbers with the lesser number given first

numerator The number above the bar in a fraction that tells how many equal parts of the whole are being considered

Pre-Assess
Write the following pairs of fractions on the board. Instruct students to write <, >, or = to compare each pair. Advise students that they may use counters, fraction bars, or number lines to help them compare.

1. $\frac{1}{3} \bigcirc \frac{2}{3}$ 2. $\frac{5}{7} \bigcirc \frac{2}{10}$

3. $\frac{3}{9} \bigcirc \frac{4}{5}$ 4. $\frac{1}{2} \bigcirc \frac{4}{8}$

Discuss each pair of fractions. Invite volunteers to explain what method they used to compare the fractions.

Common Misconception
- Students may assume that the fraction containing the larger numerator is always greater in value.
- To correct this, encourage students to use models to help them visualize the fractions.

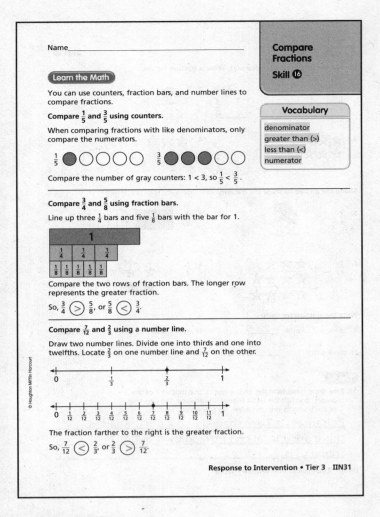

Learn the Math

Read through the first problem on student page **IIN31**. Invite students to use counters to create the model they see on the page. Discuss the meaning of each fraction, pointing out that the denominators of the fractions are alike. Ask: **What do you need to compare to find which fraction is greater?** compare the numerators of each fraction For the second and third problems, discuss ways to compare fractions with unlike denominators.

Talk Math

- **How do you know if fractions have like or unlike denominators?** Fractions with like denominators have the same number below the fraction bar. Fractions with unlike denominators do not.

- **What is the difference between comparing fractions with like denominators and comparing fractions unlike denominators?** for like denominators, compare the numerators; for unlike denominators, model each fraction to see which is greater

© Houghton Mifflin Harcourt

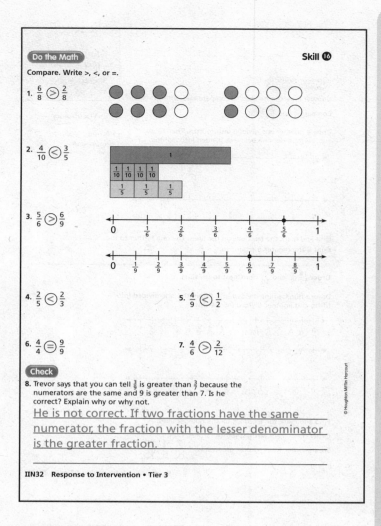

Do the Math

Guide students through Problems 1–3 on student page **IIN32**. Before assigning Problems 4–7, provide students with counters, fraction bars, and number lines. Ask: **What method will you use to compare the fractions?** Answers will vary. Have students justify their responses.

Talk Math

- **What do you know about fractions with the same number in the numerator and denominator?** They are equal to one whole, or 1.

- **How can you compare more than two fractions at a time?** Make a model for each and compare.

Check

Suggest that students solve a simpler problem. Ask: **Which fraction do you think is greater, $\frac{1}{10}$ or $\frac{1}{2}$?** Show students how this is similar to Problem 8.

Alternative Teaching Strategy

Make Number Lines to Compare Fractions

Objective To use number lines to model and compare fractions

Materials large sheets of paper

- Divide students into three groups and assign each group a number line—thirds, sixths, or ninths. Provide students with a piece of paper and ask them to work together to create a number line labeled from 0–1 that shows their assigned fractions. Each number line should be the exact same length.

- Direct students to display the three completed number lines. Ask: **Why is it important for all the number lines to be the same length?** To compare fractions accurately, you need to make sure the wholes are the same size.

- Write the following fractions on the board: $\frac{5}{6}$ and $\frac{4}{9}$. Ask: **How can you use the number lines to compare these fractions?** Find the points that represent each fraction. The fraction that is farther to the right on the number line is the greater fraction. The fraction farther to the left on the number line is the lesser fraction.

- Ask each group to use a counter to identify the point that represents the fraction on their number line. Then ask questions to guide students through the process of comparing the fractions. Ask: **Which fraction is greater?** $\frac{5}{6}$

- Repeat the activity with different fraction pairs. You may wish to repeat the exercise using fractions that are equivalent, such as $\frac{1}{3}$, $\frac{2}{6}$, and $\frac{3}{9}$.

Compare and Order Fractions
Skill 17

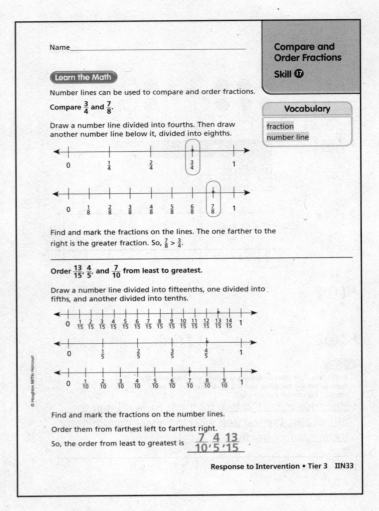

Objective

Use a number line to compare and order fractions less than 1

Vocabulary

fraction A number that names a part of a whole or a part of a group

number line A line on which numbers can be located

Pre-Assess

Draw the following number lines on the board:

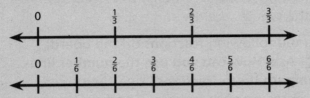

Ask students to put $\frac{3}{6}$, $\frac{1}{3}$, and $\frac{2}{3}$ in order from least to greatest, then to explain how to use the number lines to tell which is greatest. $\frac{1}{3}$, $\frac{3}{6}$, $\frac{2}{3}$; the fraction farthest to the right is the greatest.

Common Misconception

• Some students may have difficulty drawing number lines with corresponding marks for equivalent fractions.

• To correct this, remind them to make the first mark 0 and the last mark a fraction equivalent to 1. Have students line up the 0 marks and the last marks, then use a ruler to divide the number lines into equal sections.

Learn the Math

Tell students that fractions with unlike denominators can be compared using number lines. Guide students through drawing two or more number lines stacked vertically. Point out that equivalent fractions line up, as in the first

problem on student page **IIN33**. Ask: **What fraction is equivalent to $\frac{1}{4}$?** $\frac{2}{8}$ Help students work through the first problem. Guide students to see that $\frac{7}{8} > \frac{3}{4}$ is the same as $\frac{3}{4} < \frac{7}{8}$.

In the second problem, students arrange the fractions from least to greatest. Tell students that fractions can also be ordered from greatest to least.

Talk Math

• **For the second problem, how do you know that $\frac{4}{5} < \frac{13}{15}$?** It is farther to the left on the number line.

• **How would the order change if the fractions were arranged from greatest to least?** $\frac{13}{15}$, $\frac{4}{5}$, $\frac{7}{10}$

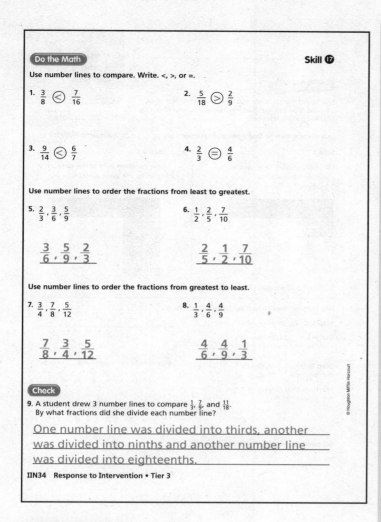

Do the Math

Have students look at student page **IIN34**. Help them create the number lines they should use for each problem. Also remind students that when they are asked to order fractions, they need to know whether the order is least to greatest or greatest to least.

Talk Math

- **What number lines would you draw for Problem 1?** one divided into eighths, and another divided into sixteenths

- **For Problem 6, in which order should you place the fractions?** least to greatest

Check

Ask: **What are the denominators of the fractions to be compared?** 3, 9, and 18

Alternative Teaching Strategy

Compare and Order Fractions

Objective To make number lines to compare 2 fractions

Materials pencils, paper, ruler, index cards labeled $\frac{1}{6}, \frac{2}{6}, \frac{3}{6}, \frac{4}{6}, \frac{5}{6}$ and $\frac{1}{12}, \frac{3}{12}, \frac{5}{12}, \frac{9}{12}, \frac{11}{12}$

- Divide students into five groups. Distribute a sixth card to each group. On the board, draw a number line divided into sixths. Only label 0 and $\frac{6}{6}$ on the number line.

- Next, draw another number line directly below this one. Make a 0 mark that lines up with the 0 mark of the first line, and then a $\frac{12}{12}$ mark that lines up with the $\frac{6}{6}$ mark of the first line. Students will use their cards to label both number lines.

- Ask each group to work together to decide which fraction with 12 as a denominator is equivalent to the fraction on their card. Have one student from each group come up to the board and label both fractions on the corresponding number lines.

- Guide students to see that they have filled in only some of the twelfths number line. Ask students to list the fractions that have not yet been placed on the number line.

- Show students how to determine where the fraction $\frac{7}{12}$ would go, then draw and label the tick mark for this fraction.

- Distribute a twelfth card to each group and have them find and label their fraction on the number line.

- Finally, ask each group to compare the fractions on their two cards. Say: **The fraction farther to the right is the greater fraction.** Ask: **Which of your fractions is greater?** Tell students to write number sentences using <, >, or =.

- Once each group correctly compares their fractions, have them trade one of their cards with another group and compare the new pair of fractions.

Model Equivalent Fractions
Skill ⑱

Objective
To model equivalent fractions

Materials
fraction bars, number lines

Vocabulary
equivalent fractions Two or more fractions that name the same amount

Pre-Assess
Write the following pairs of fractions on the board. Ask students to decide if the two fractions are equivalent. Advise students that they may use fraction bars or number lines to help them.

1. $\frac{1}{3}$ and $\frac{2}{3}$ no   2. $\frac{1}{5}$ and $\frac{2}{10}$ yes

3. $\frac{3}{9}$ and $\frac{1}{3}$ yes   4. $\frac{1}{2}$ and $\frac{4}{8}$ yes

Invite students to discuss how they determined whether the fractions were equivalent or not.

Common Misconception

- Students may believe that fractions with like numerators or like denominators are equivalent.

- To correct this, use fraction bars to display examples of fractions with the same numerator. For example, model the fractions $\frac{2}{3}$, $\frac{2}{5}$, and $\frac{2}{8}$. Then show examples of fractions with the same denominators, such as $\frac{1}{6}$, $\frac{3}{6}$, and $\frac{5}{6}$. Guide students to conclude that these fractions do not represent the same amount, and thus are not equivalent fractions.

Learn the Math
Read the definition of equivalent fractions on student page **IIN35**. Then model for students how to use fraction bars to find equivalent fractions.

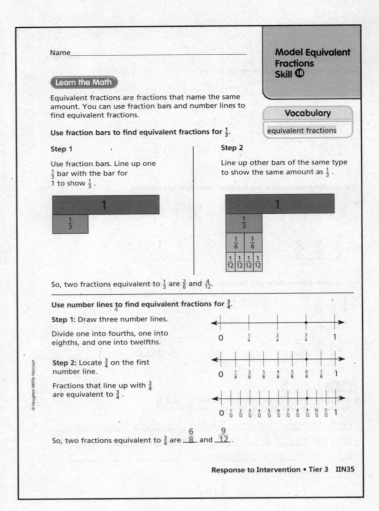

Discuss how to find equivalent fractions using a number line. You may wish to model each step for students.

Talk Math

- **Why do you need to be sure to line up the ends of the fraction bars on the left?** If they are not aligned, you may come to the wrong conclusion about whether two fractions are equivalent.

- **How is using a number line to find equivalent fractions similar to using fraction bars?** On a number line the points that are the same distance from zero are equivalent, and with fraction bars, the number of bars that reach the same length are equivalent.

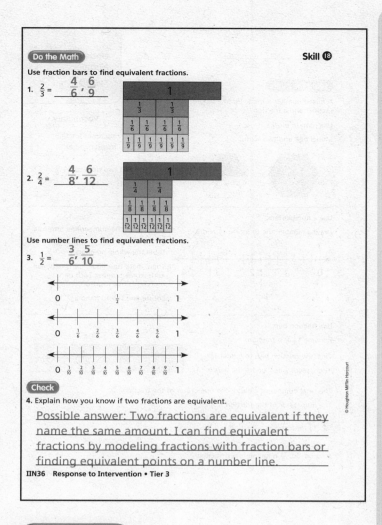

Skill 18

Use fraction bars to find equivalent fractions.

1. $\frac{2}{3} = \frac{4}{6}, \frac{6}{9}$

2. $\frac{2}{4} = \frac{4}{8}, \frac{6}{12}$

Use number lines to find equivalent fractions.

3. $\frac{1}{2} = \frac{3}{6}, \frac{5}{10}$

Check

4. Explain how you know if two fractions are equivalent.

   Possible answer: Two fractions are equivalent if they
   name the same amount. I can find equivalent
   fractions by modeling fractions with fraction bars or
   finding equivalent points on a number line.

IIN36   Response to Intervention • Tier 3

Do the Math

Guide students as they complete the problems on student page **IIN36**. Provide students with fraction bars and number lines and invite them to model each problem if they wish.

Talk Math

- **How can you find a fraction equivalent to $\frac{1}{2}$ by using fraction bars?** Possible answer: Use fractions bars to model $\frac{1}{2}$. Then use fraction bars for a different denominator to make the same length.

- **How many $\frac{1}{10}$ bars would equal $\frac{1}{2}$?** 5

Check

Ask: **Are $\frac{3}{3}$ and $\frac{8}{8}$ equivalent? How do you know?**
Yes, they both name one whole, or 1.

Alternative Teaching Strategy
Understand Equivalent Fractions

Objective To apply the concept of equal shares to equivalent fractions

Materials fraction circles

- For students struggling with the concept of equivalent fractions, applying the concept of equal shares may be helpful.

- Remind students that equivalent fractions name the same amount. Ask: **If you got $\frac{1}{2}$ of a pizza and your friend got $\frac{2}{4}$, would you have equal shares?** Write $\frac{1}{2} = \frac{2}{4}$ on the board.

- Instruct students to use fraction circles to model each fraction. Ask students to study the models. Emphasize that the models show that one half and two fourths are the same portion of the whole. Ask: **Are the fractions equivalent?** yes **If a pizza is cut into halves, and you eat one piece, and another pizza is cut into fourths and your friend eats two pieces, do you eat the same amount?** yes **How do you know?** because $\frac{1}{2}$ and $\frac{2}{4}$ are equivalent

- Challenge students to use the fraction circles to model other amounts equal to $\frac{1}{2}$ and $\frac{2}{4}$.

- Record all of the equivalent fractions on the board: $\frac{1}{2} = \frac{2}{4} = \frac{3}{6} = \frac{4}{8} = \frac{6}{12}$

- Ask: **What pattern do you see?** 1 is half of 2, 2 is half of 4, 3 is half of 6, 4 is half of 8, 6 is half of 12 **So, if you eat 1 out of 2 pieces of pizza, or 2 out of 4, or 3 out of 6, or 4 out of 8, or 6 out of 12 pieces, do you eat the same amount?** yes Say: **In each case, you eat the same fraction of the pizza—one-half.**

- Challenge students to use this pattern to come up with other equivalent fractions: 5 out of 10, 8 out of 16, 9 out of 18, 10 out of 20, and so on.

Understand Mixed Numbers
Skill ⑲

Objective
To read and write mixed numbers

Materials
pattern blocks, number lines, fraction bars

Vocabulary
improper fraction A fraction greater than 1

mixed number A number that is made up of a whole number and a fraction

Pre-Assess

Display the following pictures. Ask students to write a mixed number and an improper fraction for each picture.

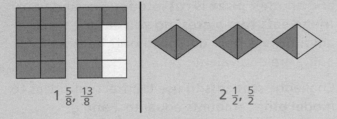

$1\frac{5}{8}, \frac{13}{8}$ $2\frac{1}{2}, \frac{5}{2}$

Common Misconception

- Students who can read and write fractions and mixed numbers may have difficulty renaming mixed numbers as improper fractions.

- To correct this, review fractions for one whole. Through multiple examples, guide students to see that there are many ways to write 1 as a fraction. Emphasize that in every case, the numerator and the denominator are the same.

Learn the Math

Read and discuss the introductory text on student page **IIN37**. Invite students to use pattern blocks to model the first example on the page. Ask: **How do you know you can write $1\frac{2}{6}$ as $1\frac{1}{3}$?** I look at the second hexagon and count the number of equal parts. I can say there are six equal parts, and 2 parts shaded. I know that $\frac{2}{6}$ is equivalent to $\frac{1}{3}$.

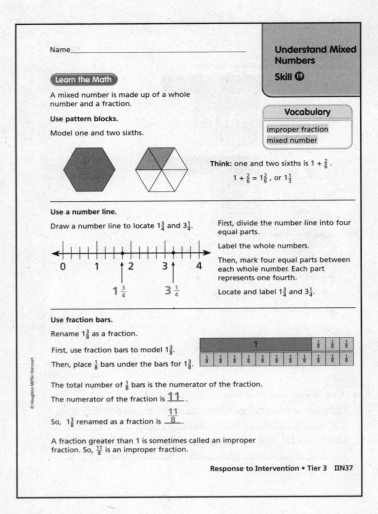

Name_____

Understand Mixed Numbers
Skill ⑲

Learn the Math

A mixed number is made up of a whole number and a fraction.

Use pattern blocks.

Model one and two sixths.

Vocabulary

improper fraction
mixed number

Think: one and two sixths is $1 + \frac{2}{6}$.

$1 + \frac{2}{6} = 1\frac{2}{6}$, or $1\frac{1}{3}$

Use a number line.

Draw a number line to locate $1\frac{3}{4}$ and $3\frac{1}{4}$.

0   1   2   3   4

$1\frac{3}{4}$ $3\frac{1}{4}$

First, divide the number line into four equal parts.

Label the whole numbers.

Then, mark four equal parts between each whole number. Each part represents one fourth.

Locate and label $1\frac{3}{4}$ and $3\frac{1}{4}$.

Use fraction bars.

Rename $1\frac{3}{8}$ as a fraction.

First, use fraction bars to model $1\frac{3}{8}$.

Then, place $\frac{1}{8}$ bars under the bars for $1\frac{3}{8}$.

The total number of $\frac{1}{8}$ bars is the numerator of the fraction.

The numerator of the fraction is **11**.

So, $1\frac{3}{8}$ renamed as a fraction is $\frac{11}{8}$.

A fraction greater than 1 is sometimes called an improper fraction. So, $\frac{11}{8}$ is an improper fraction.

Response to Intervention • Tier 3   IIN37

Explain that a number line is another way to visualize mixed numbers. Distribute number lines to students and direct them to work through the steps to locate mixed numbers on a number line.

Finally, guide students through the example for renaming mixed numbers as improper fractions. Ask: **Why is the denominator of the fraction 8?** The denominator in the fractional part of the mixed number is 8, so I use the same denominator when writing the improper fraction.

Talk Math

- **In the first problem, how many sixths make up two wholes? How do you know?** It takes twelve sixths to make up two wholes; each whole is six sixths; 6 + 6 = 12.

- **In the second problem, how do you know what each equal part between whole numbers represents?** There are 4 equal parts between each whole number, so each part is one-fourth.

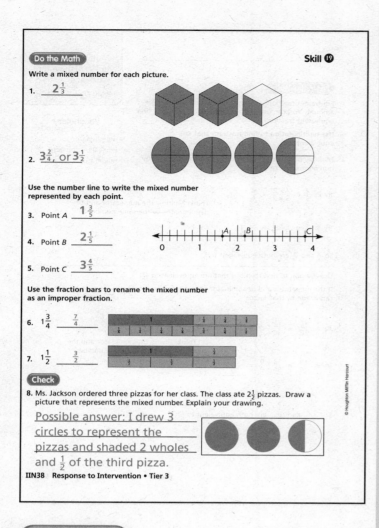

Do the Math   Skill ⑲

Write a mixed number for each picture.

1. $2\frac{1}{3}$

2. $3\frac{2}{4}$, or $3\frac{1}{2}$

Use the number line to write the mixed number represented by each point.

3. Point A $1\frac{3}{5}$

4. Point B $2\frac{1}{5}$

5. Point C $3\frac{4}{5}$

Use the fraction bars to rename the mixed number as an improper fraction.

6. $1\frac{3}{4}$ $\frac{7}{4}$

7. $1\frac{1}{2}$ $\frac{3}{2}$

Check

8. Ms. Jackson ordered three pizzas for her class. The class ate $2\frac{1}{2}$ pizzas. Draw a picture that represents the mixed number. Explain your drawing.

Possible answer: I drew 3 circles to represent the pizzas and shaded 2 wholes and $\frac{1}{2}$ of the third pizza.

IIN38   **Response to Intervention • Tier 3**

© Houghton Mifflin Harcourt

Do the Math

Guide students through the problems on student page **IIN38**. Read each direction line aloud and check that students understand what they are being asked to do.

Talk Math

- **What does a mixed number represent?** one or more wholes and part of another whole or a fraction

- **How could you use fraction bars to rename $\frac{9}{6}$ as a mixed number?** Model $\frac{9}{6}$ and then see how many $\frac{1}{6}$ bars equal 1 whole. Then, to determine the fractional part of the mixed number, count the number of remaining $\frac{1}{6}$ bars.

Check

Ask: **How can you use your drawing to write the mixed number as a fraction?** Divide each whole into halves. Count the number of halves in each whole, then count the final half. $\frac{1}{2} + \frac{1}{2} + \frac{1}{2} + \frac{1}{2} + \frac{1}{2} = \frac{5}{2}$.

Alternative Teaching Strategy

Relate Whole Numbers and Fractions

Objective To understand the relationship between whole numbers and fractions

Materials fraction bars

- Write a mixed number, such as $1\frac{1}{2}$ on the board. Ask: **How can you use fraction bars to model this number?** Use one whole bar and one $\frac{1}{2}$ bar. Invite one student to demonstrate this for the class.

- Ask: **How many $\frac{1}{2}$ bars fit under one whole?** 2 Encourage students to use fraction bars to find the answer.

- Next, write a second mixed number, such as $1\frac{1}{3}$ on the board. Ask: **How can you use fraction bars to model this number?** Use one whole bar and one $\frac{1}{3}$ bar. Again, invite one student to demonstrate.

- Ask: **How many $\frac{1}{3}$ bars fit under one whole?** 3 Encourage students to use fraction bars to find the answer.

- Repeat this process for $1\frac{1}{6}$.

- Ask: **What pattern do you notice?** Review the examples. Using $1 = \frac{2}{2}$, $1 = \frac{3}{3}$, and $1 = \frac{6}{6}$, guide students to conclude that when the numerator and the denominator of a fraction are the same, the fraction is equal to 1.

- Return to the first example. Ask: **If one whole equals two halves, how many halves make up $1\frac{1}{2}$?** 3 Lead students to see that $\frac{2}{2} + \frac{1}{2} = \frac{3}{2}$.

- Continue the activity by having students identify the improper fractions for $1\frac{1}{3}$ and $1\frac{1}{6}$ as $\frac{4}{3}$ and $\frac{7}{6}$.

Response to Intervention • Tier 3   IIN38

Multiply or Divide to Find Equivalent Fractions
Skill 20

Objective
To use multiplication and division to find equivalent fractions

Vocabulary
denominator The number below the bar in a fraction that tells how many equal parts are in the whole

equivalent fractions Two or more fractions that name the same amount

numerator The number above the bar in a fraction that tells how many equal parts of the whole are being considered

Pre-Assess
Write the following fractions on the board. Ask students to write two equivalent fractions for each. Possible answers are given.

1. $\frac{6}{30}$ $\frac{12}{60}$, $\frac{1}{5}$ 2. $\frac{14}{18}$ $\frac{7}{9}$, $\frac{28}{36}$

Display the following expressions. Ask students to find the missing number.

3. $\frac{1}{6} = \frac{?}{12}$ 2   4. $\frac{40}{40} = \frac{5}{?}$ 5

Invite students to discuss how they found the missing numbers.

Common Misconception
- Students may multiply or divide the numerator and denominator of a fraction by different numbers.

- To correct this, review the results of multiplying or dividing by 1 with students. Ask: **What is the product of 1 and a number?** the number **What is the quotient of a number divided by 1?** the number Point out that multiplying or dividing by a fraction with the same number in the numerator and denominator, such as $\frac{2}{2}$, is the same as multiplying or dividing by 1.

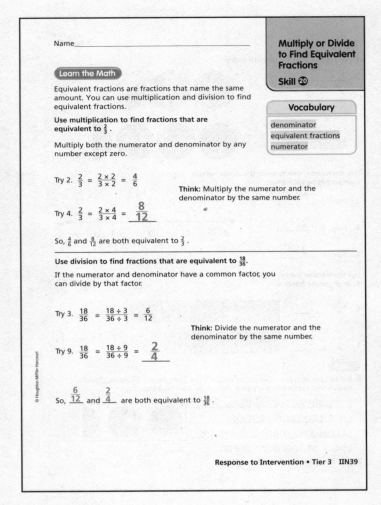

Learn the Math

Invite students to discuss what they know about equivalent fractions. Then read the introductory text on student page **IIN39**. Guide students through the first problem. Ask: **What is 2 multiplied by 4?** 8 **What number do you write in the numerator of the new fraction?** 8 **What is 3 multiplied by 4?** 12 **What number do you write in the denominator of the new fraction?** 12

Repeat this process using division to find equivalent fractions.

Talk Math

- **If you multiply the numerator of a fraction by 6, by what number will you multiply the denominator?** 6 **Why?** To find an equivalent fraction, you multiply or divide the numerator and denominator by the same number.

- **How can you check your work?** Draw a number line or use fraction bars to model each fraction to check that they are equivalent.

Do the Math

Skill ⑳

Multiply to find two equivalent fractions for each.

Possible answers are given.

1. $\frac{2}{7} = \frac{6}{21}, \frac{10}{35}$

2. $\frac{1}{8} = \frac{3}{24}, \frac{10}{80}$

3. $\frac{3}{4} = \frac{12}{16}, \frac{18}{24}$

4. $\frac{1}{3} = \frac{4}{12}, \frac{6}{18}$

5. $\frac{7}{8} = \frac{14}{16}, \frac{35}{40}$

6. $\frac{1}{4} = \frac{4}{16}, \frac{7}{28}$

Divide to find two equivalent fractions for each.

Possible answers are given.

7. $\frac{12}{24} = \frac{3}{6}, \frac{1}{2}$

8. $\frac{10}{30} = \frac{1}{3}, \frac{5}{15}$

9. $\frac{9}{36} = \frac{3}{12}, \frac{1}{4}$

10. $\frac{6}{6} = \frac{2}{2}, \frac{3}{3}$

11. $\frac{12}{20} = \frac{6}{10}, \frac{3}{5}$

12. $\frac{20}{24} = \frac{5}{6}, \frac{10}{12}$

Check

13. Are the fractions $\frac{4}{8}$ and $\frac{1}{2}$ equivalent? How do you know?

Possible answer: Yes, they are equivalent. You can multiply $\frac{1}{2}$ by $\frac{4}{4}$. $\frac{1}{2} = \frac{1 \times 4}{2 \times 4} = \frac{4}{8}$.

IIN40   Response to Intervention • Tier 3

Do the Math

Guide students as they complete the problems on student page **IIN40**. Remind students that equivalent fractions name the same amount.

Talk Math

- **Can you divide $\frac{12}{24}$ by $\frac{8}{8}$ to get an equivalent fraction? Why or why not?** No, you need to divide the numerator and denominator of a fraction by a common factor. 8 is a factor of 24, but it is not a factor of 12.

- **What are some numbers you could divide by?** 2, 3, 4, 6, and 12

Check

Ask: **Can three fractions be equivalent to each other? For Example, $\frac{1}{2}, \frac{4}{8}, \frac{3}{6}$?**

Yes, $\frac{1}{2} = \frac{1 \times 4}{2 \times 4} = \frac{4}{8}$ and $\frac{1}{2} = \frac{1 \times 3}{2 \times 3} = \frac{3}{6}$.

Alternative Teaching Strategy

Model to Find Equivalent Fractions

Objective To model multiplying and dividing to find equivalent fractions

Materials two-color counters

- Review fractions of a group. Display the following picture and invite students to identify the fraction shown. Ask: **What fraction is shaded?** two-eighths

- Circle pairs of hearts. **Ask: What fraction is shaded now?** one-fourth

- Show students you just modeled $\frac{2}{8} = \frac{2 \div 2}{8 \div 2} = \frac{1}{4}$.

- Now invite students to use two-color counters to model the fraction $\frac{8}{20}$. Instruct students to show 8 red counters and 12 yellow counters.

- **Ask: How can you use these counters to show that $\frac{8}{20}$ is equivalent to $\frac{4}{10}$?** Group the counters to show 4 pairs of red counters and 6 pairs of yellow counters. Guide students to see that they are modeling

$\frac{8}{20} = \frac{8 \div 2}{20 \div 2} = \frac{4}{10}$.

- **Ask: Can you group the counters again to show another equivalent fraction?** Yes, group the counters to show 2 groups of red counters and 3 groups of yellow counters. Guide students to see that they are modeling

$\frac{8}{20} = \frac{8 \div 4}{20 \div 4} = \frac{2}{5}$.

- Have students repeat the activity to find equivalent fractions for $\frac{6}{18}$ and $\frac{12}{24}$.

Response to Intervention • Tier 3   IIN40

Simplest Form
Skill ㉑

Objective
To reduce fractions to simplest form

Materials
fraction bars

Vocabulary
simplest form A fraction is in simplest form
when the numerator and denominator
have only 1 as their common factor

Pre-Assess

Write the following fractions on the board.
Have students write each fraction in simplest
form. Provide them with fraction bars to use, if
needed.

1. $\frac{4}{8} = \frac{1}{2}$ 2. $\frac{6}{18} = \frac{1}{3}$

3. $\frac{8}{12} = \frac{2}{3}$ 4. $\frac{2}{10} = \frac{1}{5}$

Common Misconception

- Students may divide the numerator and
  denominator of a fraction one time only, and
  conclude that it is reduced to simplest form.

- To correct this, explain to students that each
  time they divide they should look to see if
  the numerator and denominator have more
  common factors by which they can divide.

Learn the Math

Guide students through a discussion about
equivalent fractions. Have students identify that
they can find equivalent fractions by lining up
fraction bars of the same length, or by dividing
the numerator and denominator of a fraction by
the same number.

Read the text at the top of student page **IIN41**.
Explain that finding the simplest form is finding
an equivalent fraction. Explain that the difference
is that to find the simplest form students are
looking for an equivalent fraction that cannot be
divided by any number except 1.

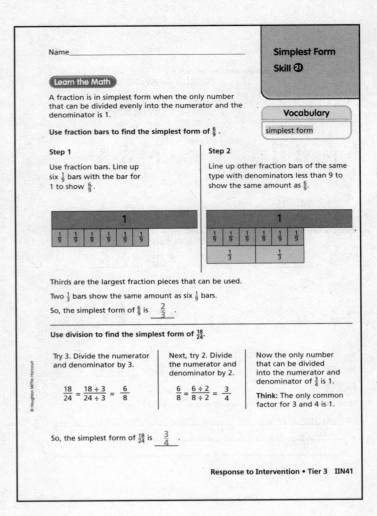

Read through the first problem with students.
Ask them to line up fraction bars with different
denominators until they find bars of the same
type that will show the same length as the original
fraction. Ask: **How do you know $\frac{2}{3}$ is equal to $\frac{6}{9}$?**
The fraction bars model the same length.

Guide students through the steps for division
in the second problem. Point out that they may
need to divide by more than one factor to find
the simplest form.

Talk Math

- **How do you know that a fraction is in simplest
  form?** A fraction is in simplest form when the
  numerator and the denominator cannot be
  divided by any number other than 1.

- **Can you divide the numerator and denominator
  by different numbers when you find simplest
  form? Why or why not?** No, that changes the
  value of the fraction. It would no longer be
  equivalent.

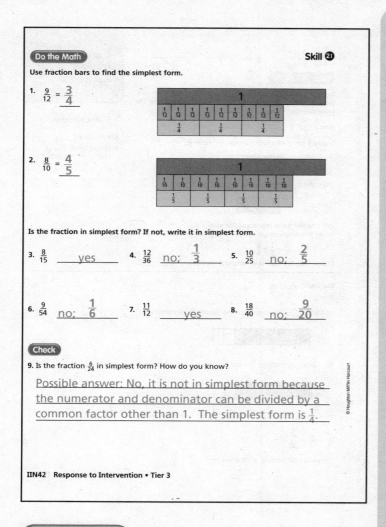

Do the Math · Skill **21**

Use fraction bars to find the simplest form.

1. $\frac{9}{12} = \frac{3}{4}$

2. $\frac{8}{10} = \frac{4}{5}$

Is the fraction in simplest form? If not, write it in simplest form.

3. $\frac{8}{15}$ __yes__ 4. $\frac{12}{36}$ __no; $\frac{1}{3}$__ 5. $\frac{10}{25}$ __no; $\frac{2}{5}$__

6. $\frac{9}{54}$ __no; $\frac{1}{6}$__ 7. $\frac{11}{12}$ __yes__ 8. $\frac{18}{40}$ __no; $\frac{9}{20}$__

Check

9. Is the fraction $\frac{6}{24}$ in simplest form? How do you know?

Possible answer: No, it is not in simplest form because the numerator and denominator can be divided by a common factor other than 1. The simplest form is $\frac{1}{4}$.

IIN42 Response to Intervention · Tier 3

© Houghton Mifflin Harcourt

Do the Math

Discuss Problem 1 on student page **IIN42**. Ask: **Are there any other fraction bars that fit under $\frac{9}{12}$?** Allow students to model with fraction bars to find the answer. Guide them to conclude that using fourths is the only option. Ask: **How many $\frac{1}{4}$ bars equal $\frac{9}{12}$?** 3 **What is the simplest form of $\frac{9}{12}$?** $\frac{3}{4}$

Talk Math

- **Explain how you determined the answer to Problem 7.** The only factor 11 and 12 have in common is 1, so the fraction is in simplest form.

- **Why might you want to write fractions in simplest form?** Possible answer: to compare them

Check

Ask: **What factors, other than 1, do 6 and 24 have in common?** 2, 3, and 6 Show why dividing by the greatest common factor will mean they only have to divide once.

Alternative Teaching Strategy
Make Factor Lists

Objective To use factor lists to find the simplest form of fractions

- Some students may struggle to identify common factors when dividing fractions to find simplest form. These students will benefit from creating factor lists before dividing.

- Write a fraction, such as $\frac{15}{18}$ on the board. Draw the following table, and ask students to copy it:

Factors of 15	Factors of 18

- Guide students to list factors of each number. Ask: **Is 2 a factor of 15?** no **Is 2 a factor of 18?** yes Write 2 below Factors of 18 in the table. **Can 2 be used to find the simplest form of this fraction?** no **Why?** 2 is not a factor of both numbers.

- Ask: **Is 3 a factor of 15?** yes **Is 3 a factor of 18?** yes Write 3 in both columns of the table.

- Continue to work your way through the factors 4, 5, 6, 7, 8, and 9, asking students to identify if the number is a factor of one or both of the numbers, and listing it in the appropriate column(s).

- Ask: **Which number is a factor of both 15 and 18?** 3 **How can you use this number to find the fraction in simplest form?** Divide 15 and 18 by 3. Invite a student to the board to record the division: $\frac{15}{18} = \frac{15 \div 3}{18 \div 3} = \frac{5}{6}$

- Create a factor list for 5 and 6. When students conclude that there are no common factors for 5 and 6 aside from 1, ask: **Is this fraction in simplest form?** yes

- Repeat the activity for a fraction with a numerator and denominator that have more than one common factor, guiding students as they work through several rounds of division.

Add and Subtract Fractions
Skill ㉒

Objective
To add and subtract fractions with like denominators using models or pictures

Vocabulary
simplest form A fraction is in simplest form when the numerator and denominator have only 1 as their common factor

Pre-Assess
Write $\frac{2}{5} + \frac{2}{5}$ and $\frac{7}{8} - \frac{3}{8}$ on the board. Ask students to use models to solve the problems. Instruct them to write the answers in simplest form. Ask: **What is $\frac{2}{5} + \frac{2}{5}$?** $\frac{4}{5}$ **What is $\frac{7}{8} - \frac{3}{8}$?** $\frac{4}{8}$, or $\frac{1}{2}$

Common Misconception

• Students may recognize that fractions with like denominators are added or subtracted by adding or subtracting numerators. However, they may also incorrectly add or subtract denominators.

• To correct this, explain that when fractions with like denominators are added or subtracted, only the numbers in the numerator change.

Learn the Math

Review fractions with like denominators with students.

Go through the first problem on student page **IIN43**. Help students add the fractions with like denominators using a model. Ask: **How do you know how many parts to shade first?** The number of parts shaded is equal to the numerator of the first addend. **How do you know how many parts to shade next?** The number of parts shaded is equal to the numerator of the second addend. Guide students to see that the total number of shaded parts is the numerator of the sum. The denominator is the total number of parts.

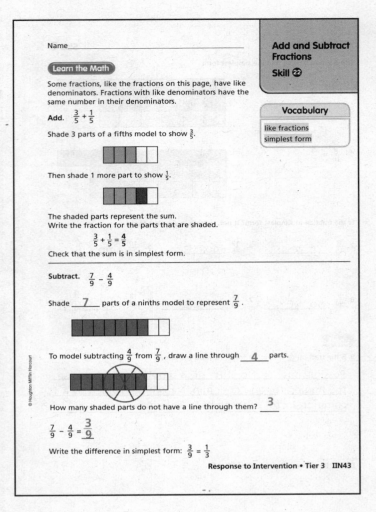

Have students look at the second problem. First, shade the parts to represent the first numerator. Then, model subtraction of the other numerator by circling the group being subtracted, and then crossing out the group. Remind students that crossing out a part on the model will not change the denominator. Some students may think that crossing out a part changes the denominator. For those students, erase the shading to show that the denominator doesn't change.

Talk Math

• **In the second example, how do you know how many parts of the model to shade?** The number of shaded parts is equal to the numerator of the fraction you are subtracting from.

• **Are the denominators added or subtracted when adding or subtracting like fractions?** no

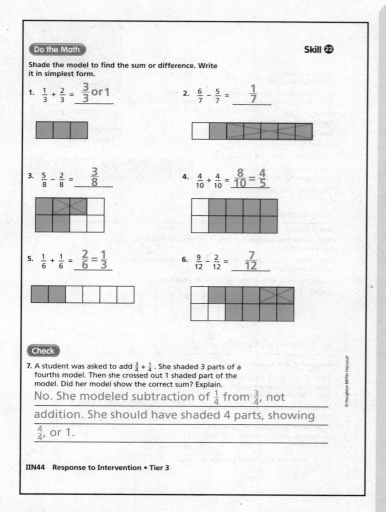

Objective To add and subtract fractions with like denominators using fraction models

Materials fraction bars

- Tell students that they are going to model addition of fractions with like denominators using fraction bars for sixths. Ask: **How many sixths make 1 whole?** 6 **What fraction does each bar represent?** $\frac{1}{6}$

- Instruct students to model $\frac{1}{6}$ by using 1 bar. Next ask them to model $\frac{5}{6}$ by using 4 more bars. Direct the students to combine and count the bars used. Ask: **Is the sum greater than, less than or equal to 1?** less than **What fraction do the fraction bars represent?** $\frac{5}{6}$ **What is $\frac{1}{6} + \frac{4}{6}$?** $\frac{5}{6}$

- Next, tell students that they are going to model subtraction. Ask them to remove $\frac{2}{6}$ from the $\frac{5}{6}$. Ask: **What fraction do the remaining fraction bars represent?** $\frac{3}{6}$ **What is $\frac{5}{6} - \frac{2}{6}$?** $\frac{3}{6}$ Direct students to write the difference in simplest form, $\frac{1}{2}$.

- Put students in pairs or groups. Write these problems on the board and ask pairs to solve each: $\frac{6}{6} - \frac{1}{6} = \frac{5}{6}$; $\frac{2}{6} + \frac{2}{6} = \frac{4}{6}$, or $\frac{2}{3}$; $\frac{4}{6} - \frac{1}{6} = \frac{3}{6}$, or $\frac{1}{2}$; $\frac{4}{6} - \frac{3}{6} = \frac{1}{6}$; $\frac{5}{6} + \frac{1}{6} = \frac{6}{6}$, or 1; $\frac{3}{6} + \frac{3}{6} = \frac{6}{6}$, or 1. Instruct pairs to record their answers and share them with the class. Extend the activity using eighths or twelfths models, and new number sentences.

Do the Math

Have students look at student page **IIN44**. Tell them to first identify if they are adding or subtracting. Explain the steps to model addition or subtraction as students perform them. Check to make sure students understand the correct order of the steps.

Talk Math

- **Which are subtraction problems?** 2, 3, and 6

- **What is the first step in either addition or subtraction?** Shade the model to represent the first fraction.

Check

Guide students to see that crossing out a part is the same as removing the shading. Tell them that adding a fraction requires shading more parts of the model.

Rename Fractions and Mixed Numbers

Skill 23

Objective
To rename fractions as mixed numbers and mixed numbers as fractions

Materials
fraction bars, number lines

Vocabulary
fraction A number that names a part of a whole or a part of a group

mixed number A number that is made up of a whole number and a fraction

Pre-Assess

Direct students to model $1\frac{3}{8}$ using fraction bars or a number line. Then, ask them to rename the number as a fraction. Also ask students to model $\frac{9}{7}$ using fraction bars, then to rename it as a mixed number.

Common Misconception

- Students may confuse the operations to use for renaming fractions and for renaming mixed numbers.

- To correct this, remind them that a fraction has two numbers separated by a fraction bar, which indicates division. Ask them to rewrite some fractions greater than 1 as division problems, such as $\frac{25}{8} = 25 \div 8$.

Learn the Math

Tell students that all fractions greater than 1 can be rewritten as mixed numbers and all mixed numbers can be rewritten as fractions.

Go through the first problem on student page **IIN45**. Then, direct students to look at the second problem. Have them locate the fraction and the mixed number on the number line.

Note that a number line used for renaming must be marked as the same unit as the fraction, in this case fifths. If the fraction was $\frac{13}{6}$, a number line marked in sixths would be necessary.

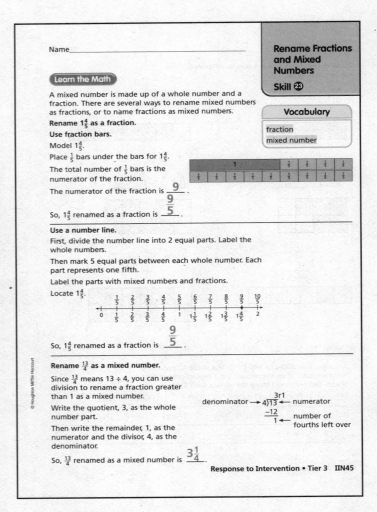

For the third problem, guide students to see how the numbers in the division problem relate to the mixed number. Take students through the steps to rename a fraction as a mixed number. You may also ask students to model this mixed number using fraction bars. Guide them to see that either modeling or division can be used to rename fractions and mixed numbers.

Talk Math

- **What does a mixed number represent?** the sum of a whole number and a fraction

- **When a mixed number is renamed as a fraction, is the numerator greater than or less than the denominator?** greater than

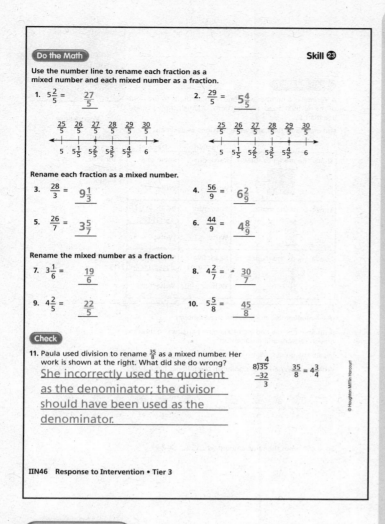

Do the Math

Guide students through Problems 1 and 2 on student page **IIN46**. For Problems 3–10, remind students that they can choose any method for renaming. Tell students that using more that one method can help them to check their answers.

Talk Math

• **Which operation does the fraction bar in a fraction represent?** division

• **Name two models that can be used to rename mixed numbers.** Possible answer: fraction bars and number lines

Check

Ask: **Which part of the division problem should be the denominator of the mixed number?** the divisor

Alternative Teaching Strategy

Rename Fractions and Mixed Numbers

Objective To use models to rename fractions as mixed numbers and mixed numbers as fractions

• Tell students they are going to model a fraction greater than 1. On the board, draw 2 circles divided into eighths. Shade 11 of the eighths pieces, 8 in the first circle, and 3 in the other. Ask: **How many eighths are shaded?** 11 Ask: **How would you say and write this number as a fraction?** eleven eighths; $\frac{11}{8}$

• Guide students to see that this fraction is greater than 1. Ask: **How many eigths make a whole?** 8 **Is $\frac{11}{8}$ more than one whole?** yes

• Ask: **How many wholes and how many eighths do you have?** 1 whole, 3 eighths. **How would you say this?** one and three eighths **How would you write this?** $1\frac{3}{8}$ Write $\frac{11}{8} = 1\frac{3}{8}$ on the board.

• Repeat the activity for $2\frac{1}{8}$. Then draw circles divided into sixths and have students rename $1\frac{4}{6}$ as a fraction and rename $\frac{13}{6}$ as a mixed number.

Relate Fractions and Decimals
Skill 24

Objective
To model, read, and record fractions as decimals

Materials
decimal models, number lines

Vocabulary
decimal A number with one or more digits to the right of the decimal point

decimal point A symbol used to separate dollars from cents in a money amount and to separate the ones and the tenths place in a decimal

fraction A number that names a part of a whole or a part of a group

tenth One of ten equal parts

hundredth One of one hundred equal parts

Pre-Assess
Draw a tenths model on the board. Ask: **How many equal parts are in the model?** ten Shade one tenth. **How many parts are shaded?** one **What fraction does the model show?** $\frac{1}{10}$ **What decimal does the model show?** 0.1

Display the following models. Ask students to write the fraction and decimal shown by each model.

1. 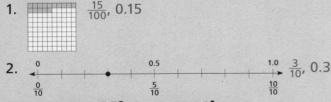 $\frac{15}{100}$, 0.15

2. $\frac{3}{10}$, 0.3

Common Misconception

- Students may place the decimal point in the wrong place, writing a whole number rather than a decimal.

- To correct this, remind students to always place the decimal point between the ones digit and the tenths digit. Emphasize using a zero in the ones place to show there are no ones.

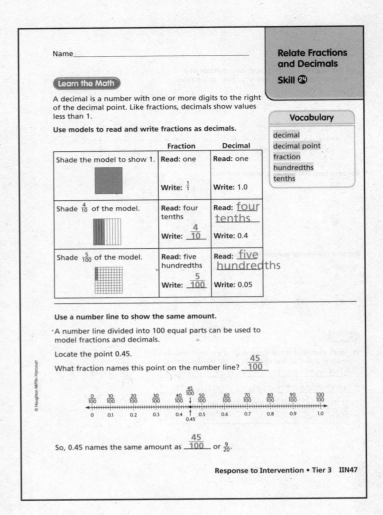

Learn the Math
Read the introductory text on student page **IIN47.** Then discuss the models in the first problem. For each model, ask: **How many equal parts are there in the model?** 1, 10, 100 **How many parts are shaded?** 1, 4, 5 Then read the values shown by each model.

Discuss the next problem with students. Be sure students understand that the fraction and decimal in the model name the same amount.

Talk Math

- **What do you notice about the way the fractions and decimals are read and written?** They sound the same when you read them, but you write them in a different way.

- **Why are these fractions and decimals read the same way?** The denominator of the fraction relates to the place value of the rightmost digit that is not a zero, in the decimal.

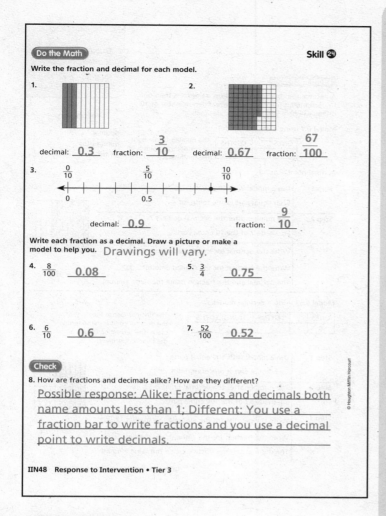

Alternative Teaching Strategy

Fractions and Decimals with Money

Objective To model and write decimals and fractions in tenths and hundredths using money

Materials dimes, pennies

- Students who struggle with the relationship between fractions and decimals may understand the concept when presented in terms of money.

- Provide pairs of students with dimes and pennies. Ask: **How many dimes make one dollar?** 10 **What fraction of the dollar is one dime?** $\frac{1}{10}$ **How do you write the value of a dime with a decimal point and a dollar sign?** $0.10

- Write a list of items with prices that are multiples of ten cents. Ask students to tell how many dimes are required to purchase each item. Then instruct students to write the cost as a decimal and then as a fraction of a dollar.

- Ask: **How many pennies make one dollar?** 100 **What fraction of the dollar is one penny?** $\frac{1}{100}$ **How do you write the value of a penny with a decimal point and a dollar sign?** $0.01

- Write a list of items with prices that are less than a dollar. Ask students to tell how many pennies are required to purchase each item. Then instruct students to write the cost as a decimal and then as a fraction of a dollar. Make sure to include items that cost less than $0.10.

Do the Math

Have students look at student page **IIN48**. Discuss each of the models in Problems 1–3. For Problems 4–7, ask students to describe how they might draw a picture to help them visualize the fractions. Then help students complete the page.

Talk Math

- **How does seeing the number 10 or 100 in the denominator of the fraction help you write a related decimal?** If the fraction has 100 in the denominator, the decimal will have two digits to the right of the decimal point. If it has 10, the decimal will have 1 digit to the right of the decimal point.

- **What does the 0 to the left of the decimal point tell you?** There are zero ones.

Check

Say: **one tenth.** Ask: **Did I just just name a fraction or a decimal?** both **How could you tell which one I meant?** by seeing it written down

Decimal Models
Skill ㉕

Objective
To model and write decimals for tenths and hundredths

Materials
decimal models

Vocabulary
decimal A number with one or more digits to the right of the decimal point

hundredth One of one hundred equal parts

tenth One of ten equal parts

Pre-Assess
Draw a tenths model on the board and shade three tenths. Ask: **How many parts are shaded?** 3 **How many parts are there in all?** 10 **What fraction does the model show?** three tenths **What decimal does the model show?** three tenths **How would you write this decimal?** 0.3

Draw hundredths models for 0.25 and 0.78 on the board. Ask students to write the fraction and decimal for the shaded part of each model.

Common Misconception
- Students may confuse tens and tenths and hundreds and hundredths.

- To correct this, write the numbers 200, 20, 0.2 and 0.02 on the board. Read each number aloud and guide students to identify the place value of each digit. Emphasize each of the different values: two hundreds, two tens, two tenths, and two hundredths. You may wish to repeat the activity with additional values to check that students have grasped the concept.

Learn the Math
Read the first problem on student page **IIN49**. Point out the positions of the decimal point and the digits 0 and 7 in 0.7.

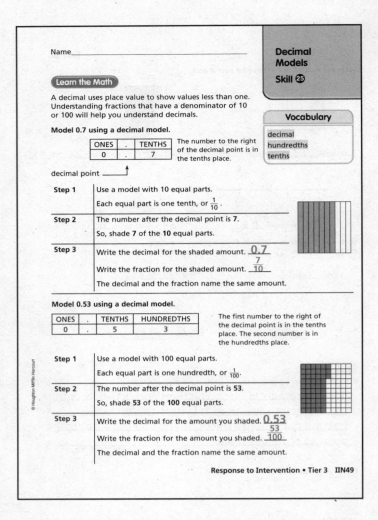

Then guide the class through the steps to model the decimal. Clarify that both the decimal and the fraction are read as "seven tenths."

Read and discuss the second problem. Ask: **How many equal parts are there in the model?** 100 **Why do you shade 53 parts?** Each part is one hundredth, so you shade 53 parts to show 53 hundredths.

Talk Math
- **What do the numerator and denominator of a fraction represent?** The numerator names the number of shaded parts and the denominator names the total number of equal parts.

- **How are fractions and decimals related?** Possible response: They both name numbers less than 1.

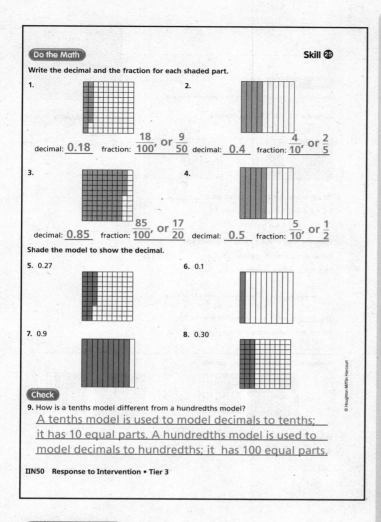

Do the Math

Discuss each model in Problems 1–4 on student page **IIN50**. For Problems 5–8, ask students to read each decimal aloud. This will help them visualize the answer. Then guide students to complete the page.

Talk Math

- **How do you know what decimal is shown?** I count the shaded parts and the total number of equal parts.

- **How can you write each decimal as a fraction?** I write the number of shaded parts as the numerator, and the number of equal parts as the denominator.

Check

Guide students to model one tenth and ten hundredths and compare the models. Ask: **How do one tenth and ten hundredths compare?** They are equivalent.

Alternative Teaching Strategy

Relate Fractions and Decimals

Objective To model and write tenths as decimals and fractions

Materials fraction strips, decimal models

- Have students work in pairs. Distribute fraction strips for tenths and ask pairs to model one whole. Then have pairs model one whole on a tenths model. Ask: **How many tenths do you need to model 1?** 10 tenths

- Remind students that both fractions and decimals name numbers less than 1. Explain that any number less than 1 can be written as both a fraction and a decimal.

- Invite students to model one tenth with fraction strips and then on a tenths model. Ask: **What fraction does the model show?** $\frac{1}{10}$ **Why do you write 1 in the numerator?** to show how many parts are being counted **Why do you write 10 in the denominator?** to show how many parts there are in all **What decimal does the tenths model show?** 0.1 **Where do you write the 1?** to the right of the decimal point, in the tenths place

- Next, invite students to model nine tenths as a fraction and as a decimal. Ask: **What fraction does the model show?** $\frac{9}{10}$ **What decimal does the model show?** 0.9

- Ask students to return to the models of one whole. Challenge them to write and read the fraction and decimal shown by the models. Guide students to conclude that $\frac{10}{10}$ and 1.0 (or 1) are equivalent.

Compare Decimals
Skill ㉖

Objective
To compare decimals using models and number lines

Materials
base-ten blocks

Vocabulary
decimal A number with one or more digits to the right of the decimal point

number line A line on which numbers can be located

Pre-Assess
Show students a number line marked at every hundredth from 1.00 to 1.50. Ask them to use this number line, or models if they choose, to determine which is the greater decimal in each of the following pairs of decimals:
1.33, 1.30 1.33; 1.05, 1.5 1.5; 1.12, 1.21 1.21; 1.49, 1.48 1.49 1.0, 1.1 1.1.

Have students explain how they know which number is greater.

Common Misconception
• Some students may have difficulty writing or recognizing equivalent decimals.

• To correct this, remind students that placing a zero at the end of a decimal will not change its value. Ask them to practice writing equivalent decimals for 7.9, 3.0, 4.2, and 5.1. 7.90, 3.00, 4.20, 5.10

Learn the Math

The first problem on student page **IIN51** shows decimal models in tenths. This problem also uses the greater than and less than symbols. Guide students to see that either symbol can be used to write a number sentence that shows the relationship between two decimals.

In the second problem, students are asked to compare a number with a digit in the tenths

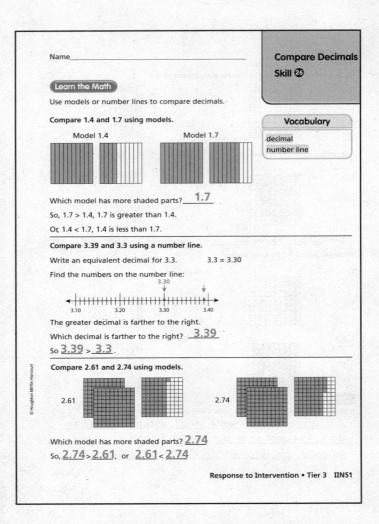

Learn the Math

Use models or number lines to compare decimals.

Compare 1.4 and 1.7 using models.

Model 1.4   Model 1.7

Which model has more shaded parts? __1.7__

So, 1.7 > 1.4, 1.7 is greater than 1.4.

Or, 1.4 < 1.7, 1.4 is less than 1.7.

Compare 3.39 and 3.3 using a number line.

Write an equivalent decimal for 3.3.   3.3 = 3.30

Find the numbers on the number line:

3.10   3.20   3.30   3.40

The greater decimal is farther to the right.

Which decimal is farther to the right? __3.39__

So __3.39__ > __3.3__.

Compare 2.61 and 2.74 using models.

2.61   2.74

Which model has more shaded parts? __2.74__

So, __2.74__ > __2.61__, or __2.61__ < __2.74__

Vocabulary

decimal
number line

Response to Intervention • Tier 3   IIN51

place to a number with digits in both the tenths and hundredths places. Some students may not recognize immediately that 3.3 is the same as 3.30. Help students see that 3.3 and 3.30 are equivalent decimals. Assist students in finding the decimals on the number line.

The third problem shows models in hundredths. 261 small squares are shaded to show 2.61.

Students can also use base-ten blocks to model each decimal. In this case, a hundreds block represents 1, a tens block represents a tenth, and a ones block represents a hundredth. As an example, 2.61 could be modeled with 2 hundred blocks, 6 tens blocks, and 1 ones block.

Talk Math

• **Why are 3.3 and 3.30 equivalent decimals?** Attaching a zero to the end of a decimal does not change its value.

• **How do you find 3.39 on the number line?** Count 9 to the right of 3.30, or 1 to the left of 3.40.

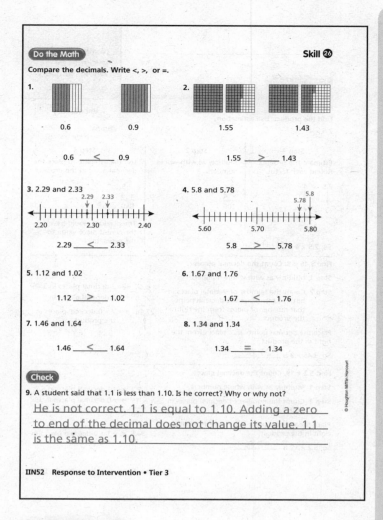

Do the Math — Skill 26

Compare the decimals. Write <, >, or =.

1. 0.6   0.9
   0.6 < 0.9

2. 1.55   1.43
   1.55 > 1.43

3. 2.29 and 2.33
   2.29 < 2.33

4. 5.8 and 5.78
   5.8 > 5.78

5. 1.12 and 1.02
   1.12 > 1.02

6. 1.67 and 1.76
   1.67 < 1.76

7. 1.46 and 1.64
   1.46 < 1.64

8. 1.34 and 1.34
   1.34 = 1.34

Check

9. A student said that 1.1 is less than 1.10. Is he correct? Why or why not?

   He is not correct. 1.1 is equal to 1.10. Adding a zero to end of the decimal does not change its value. 1.1 is the same as 1.10.

IIN52   Response to Intervention • Tier 3

Do the Math

For Problems 3 and 4 on student page **IIN52**, ask students to mark the decimals on the number lines, rather than make mental comparisons. Direct students to use blocks for modeling or draw number lines to solve Problems 5 and 6.

Talk Math

- **In Problem 2, how many hundredth squares are shaded to show 1.55?** 155 **To show 1.43?** 143

- **What is an equivalent decimal to 5.8?** 5.80

- **Is 5.80 to the right or left of 5.78 on a number line?** to the right

Check

Ask: **Does attaching a zero to the end of a decimal change its value?** no

---

Alternative Teaching Strategy

Comparing Money Values

Objective To compare decimals using money

Materials play money (dollars, dimes, pennies)

- Have students work in pairs. Explain that they are going to use money to practice comparing decimals.

- Tell students they will model and compare various money amounts by using play money. Tell students to use the fewest number of coins as possible to show each amount.

- Direct pairs to show $1.52 on the left side of their work space, using 1 dollar, 5 dimes and 2 pennies. Then ask them to show $1.59 on the right side of their work space.

- Ask: **How many dollar bills are in $1.52?** 1 **In $1.59?** 1 **How many dimes are in $1.52?** 5 **In $1.59?** 5 Explain that since the dollar bill and dime amounts are the same in each, the money value with more pennies is greater. **Which has more pennies?** $1.59 Say: **$1.59 is greater than $1.52.** Write $1.59 > $1.52 on the board.

- Next ask the pairs to show $2.17 on the left side of their work space and $2.20 on the right side of their work space. Ask: **How many dollars are in each?** 2 **How many dimes are in $2.17?** 1 **How many dimes are in $2.20?** 2 Explain that since the models do not have an equal number of dimes, the pennies do not need to be compared. The money value with more dimes is greater **Which is greater?** $2.20 **Why?** There are more dimes in $2.20 than in $2.17.

- Have students use money to compare the following amounts using < and > symbols: $1.33 and $1.43, $1.00 and $1.01, $0.52 and $0.60, $2.89 and $2.84. $1.33 < $1.43, $1.00 < $1.01, $0.52 < $0.60, $2.89 > $2.84

- Ask groups to share their findings with the class.

Multiply Decimals by Whole Numbers
Skill ㉗

Objective
To multiply decimals by whole numbers

Vocabulary
decimal A number with one or more digits to the right of the decimal point

Pre-Assess
Ask students to solve the following problems:

$5.4 \times 5 = 27.0$ $3.2 \times 3 = 9.6$ $4.11 \times 15 = 61.65$

For each problem, ask them to show their work and explain how they found the product.

Common Misconception

- Some students may not understand where to place the decimal point in the product after multiplying a decimal and a whole number.

- To correct this, remind students to look for the total number of decimal places in the factors. The decimal point should be placed so that the same number of decimal places shows in the product. Estimation may be used to check that the answer is reasonable.

Learn the Math

Explain that the problems shown on student page **IIN53** show the steps for multiplying decimals by 1- or 2-digit whole numbers.

Read the steps for the first problem. Show students that 10.0 is the same as 10. This answer is the most reasonable since it has the closest value to 12, the estimate. Guide students to rule out 1.00 and 100. as answers.

For the second problem, guide students to see that there is a total of two decimal places in both factors, so the product should also show two decimal places. The decimal point should therefore be positioned so that the digit farthest to the right is in the hundredths place.

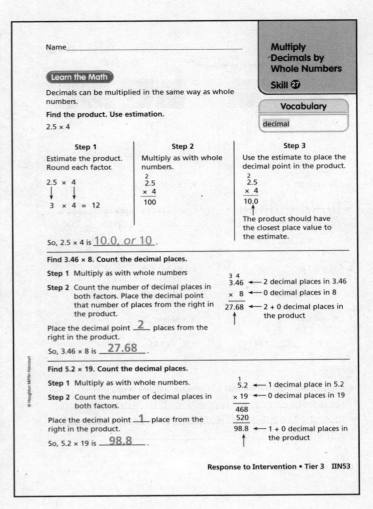

The example in the third problem shows the same procedure. Help students see that the product in the third problem should show the digit 8 in the tenths place.

Instruct students to write out all their work clearly when they solve multiplication problems with decimals. Explain that this will help them see what mistake they might have made when checking their answer against an estimate. Discuss placement of the decimal point in each case.

Talk Math

- **What is the total number of decimal places in the factors in the problem 3.46 × 8?** two

- **In the problem 5.2 × 19, how many places will you move to place the decimal point?** one

- **Should you move from the right to the left, or from the left to right of the product when moving the decimal point?** from the right to the left

---

Do the Math

Have students look at the problems on student page IIN54. Remind students to first multiply, and then place the decimal point in the product.

Talk Math

• In Problem 7, what is your product before placing the decimal point? 330

• Once you place the decimal point, what do you notice about the decimal values? There are no tenths or hundredths.

Check

Ask: **What whole numbers might you use to estimate the product?** 1×3 **Is this estimate close to 39.6?** no Guide students in positioning the decimal point correctly.

© Houghton Mifflin Harcourt

Alternative Teaching Strategy

Multiply Decimals and Whole Numbers

Objective To multiply decimals and whole numbers using hundredths and tenths models

Materials grid paper, lined paper, colored pencils

• Tell students to make several hundredths models on grid paper by outlining 10-by-10 squares. Tell them they will use these to multiply decimals and whole numbers.

• Write 0.81×3 on the board. Tell students to find the product by shading 81 hundredths with a color. Do this two more times, each with a new color. Guide them to fill a whole hundredths model before coloring parts of another.

• When students are finished, ask: **What is the total number of hundredths shaded?** 243 **How do you write this as a decimal?** 2.43 Write $0.81 \times 3 = 2.43$.

• Ask: **What is the total number of decimal places in the factors?** two Show students that there are also two decimal places shown in the product.

• Next tell students to make at least 15 tenths models on lined paper by outlining 10 rectangular spaces for each tenth.

• Write 0.9×12 on the board. Instruct students to find the product by shading 9 tenths, 12 times. When they are finished, ask: **What is the total number of tenths shaded?** 108 **How do you write this as a decimal?** 10.8 Write $0.9 \times 12 = 10.8$.

• Again, ask: **What is the total number of decimal places in the factors?** one **How many decimal places are there in the product?** 1

• Write these problems on the board, and tell students to use models to solve them:

$0.3 \times 18 =$ 5.4 $1.2 \times 11 =$ 13.2

$0.43 \times 5 =$ 2.15 $1.89 \times 4 =$ 7.56

Response to Intervention • Tier 3   IIN54

Understand Percent

Skill 28

Objective
To model percents and write percents as fractions and decimals

Materials
10 × 10 grids

Vocabulary
percent The ratio of a number to 100 or "per hundred"

Pre-Assess
Write the following on the board: 50%, 20%, 33%, 80%. Ask students to explain what *percent* means. "per hundred," or a ratio of a number to 100 Then tell the students to model each percent, and write each as a decimal and as a fraction in simplest form. 0.50, 0.20, 0.33, 0.80; $\frac{1}{2}$, $\frac{1}{5}$, $\frac{33}{100}$, $\frac{4}{5}$

Common Misconception

- Students may have trouble identifying the amount that is the whole, or 100%.

- To correct this, tell students that 100% of any number is that number. Point out that 100% of 2 is 2, and 100% of 99 is 99.

Learn the Math

Tell students that the % symbol is always read "percent." Explain that percent means "per hundred," and describes part of a whole.

The first problem on student page **IIN55** uses a 10-by-10 grid to show percents. Help students see that 100% is 100 out of 100, or all of the whole and 50% is 50 out of 100, or half of the whole.

Guide students through writing percents as fractions. Tell them that they can first write the percents as parts of 100, and then simplify. Guide students through writing the percents as decimals in the second problem.

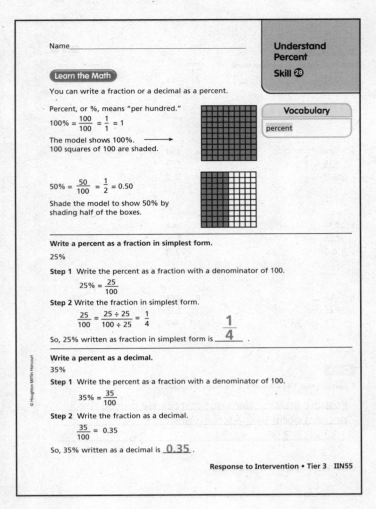

Explain that to write any percent as a decimal, students should first write it as a fraction with a denominator of 100. You may have students shade hundredths models to show 10%, 25%, 35% and 80%.

Then show students examples of single digit percents, such as 1% and 8%, and make sure they understand the difference between 0.8 and 0.08.

Talk Math

- **What fraction with a denominator of 100 is equal to 0.35?** $\frac{35}{100}$

- **Can this fraction be written as a percent?** yes **What is the percent?** 35%

- **If you were writing 35% as a fraction in simplest form, what would you do?** Divide both the numerator and denominator of the fraction $\frac{35}{100}$ by 5; $\frac{7}{20}$.

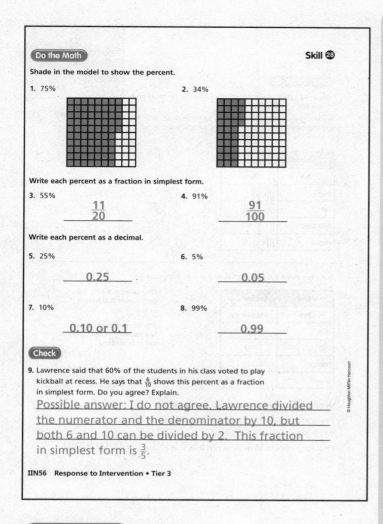

Do the Math — Skill 28

Shade in the model to show the percent.

1. 75%   2. 34%

Write each percent as a fraction in simplest form.

3. 55% $\dfrac{11}{20}$ 4. 91% $\dfrac{91}{100}$

Write each percent as a decimal.

5. 25%   0.25   6. 5%   0.05

7. 10%   0.10 or 0.1   8. 99%   0.99

Check

9. Lawrence said that 60% of the students in his class voted to play kickball at recess. He says that $\dfrac{6}{10}$ shows this percent as a fraction in simplest form. Do you agree? Explain.

Possible answer: I do not agree. Lawrence divided the numerator and the denominator by 10, but both 6 and 10 can be divided by 2. This fraction in simplest form is $\dfrac{3}{5}$.

IIN56   Response to Intervention • Tier 3

© Houghton Mifflin Harcourt

Do the Math

Allow students to use 10 × 10 grids for Problems 3–8 on student page **IIN56**. For Problem 6, ask them to say the fraction before converting it to a decimal.

Talk Math

- For Problem 4, what fraction with a denominator of 100 is equal to 91%? $\dfrac{91}{100}$ Can this fraction be simplified? no

- For Problem 7, what is another way to write the decimal 0.10? 0.1

Check

Ask students to first check and see if the fraction is equivalent to 60%. When students realize that it is, ask: **Is the fraction in simplest form?** no Guide students to further simplify the fraction.

Alternative Teaching Strategy

Understand Percent

Objective To explore percents using models

Materials grid paper and pencils, counters

- Place students in groups of 3. Explain that they will learn about percent, which means "per hundred."

- Say: **100% means 100 out of 100 and 95% means 95 out of 100. What does 90% mean?** 90 out of 100

- Tell groups to shade 90 out of 100 squares in a 10 × 10 grid. Ask: **How do you write this as a decimal?** 0.90 **What is 90 out of 100 as a fraction in simplest form?** $\dfrac{9}{10}$

- Direct groups to write 75%, 50%, 40% and 30% as decimals and fractions in simplest form. 0.75, 0.50, 0.40, 0.30; $\dfrac{3}{4}$, $\dfrac{1}{2}$, $\dfrac{2}{5}$, $\dfrac{3}{10}$ Check answers as a class.

- Next show students a group of 100 counters. Tell one student to remove 15 of the counters. Ask: **What fraction of the counters was removed?** $\dfrac{15}{100}$ Direct students to look back at their earlier work, and match this fraction with a percent. Ask: **What percent of the counters was taken away?** 15%

- Then ask one student to take 9 counters. Ask: **What fraction of the counters was taken away?** $\dfrac{9}{100}$ Guide students to write a percent and a decimal for this fraction. 9%; 0.09

- Point out that whether writing a percent as a fraction or a decimal, the first step is to write a fraction with a denominator of 100.

Response to Intervention • Tier 3   IIN56

Read a Frequency Table
Skill 29

Objective
To read a frequency table

Materials
colored pencils or colored highlighters

Vocabulary
frequency The number of times something occurs

numerical data Data that can be measured or counted

survey A method of gathering information from a group

Pre-Assess

Draw the following frequency table on the board:

Favorite Color Survey	
Color	Votes
red	15
blue	43
green	32
yellow	10

Ask: **How many people were surveyed?** 100
Ask: **Which color got the fewest votes?** yellow
Ask: **How many more votes did blue get than green?** 11

Common Misconception

• Students may have trouble reading the rows of the frequency table correctly.

• To correct this, suggest that students shade each row of the table a different color, or mark the rows with different symbols.

Learn the Math

Tell students that frequency tables are used to show numerical data, information that can be measured or counted. Explain that the tables can help to organize and compare survey data.

Name_____

Learn the Math

Frequency tables show information that can be measured or counted.

Jim asked each student in his class to name their favorite pet and recorded the answers. First, he made a tally table to show the results of his survey.

Vocabulary
frequency
numerical data
survey

Favorite Pet Survey	
Pet	Tally
dog	IIII IIII
cat	IIII IIII III
hamster	II
snake	III

Then Jim made a frequency table. It shows numerical data.

Favorite Pet Survey	
Pet	Frequency
dog	10
cat	13
hamster	2
snake	3

One column shows the pets students chose.

The other column shows the number of times each pet was chosen.

Frequency is the number of times something was chosen, or occurred.

Use the frequency table to answer each question.

How many students did Jim survey? __28 students__

Which pet was chosen most often? ____cat____

How many more children chose cats than snakes? __10 more children__

Response to Intervention • Tier 3   IIN57

Direct students to the tally table and frequency table on student page **IIN57**. Use the tables to point out common features: two columns, a label for each column, a title. Draw attention to the frequency table and the fact that numbers, not tally marks, are used to represent data. Ask: **How many times was *hamster* chosen as a favorite pet?** 2 Guide the students to find *hamster* in the frequency table, and look for the corresponding number in the frequency column.

Tell students that frequency tables can be used for any type of data that can be counted, not just survey data.

Talk Math

• **What type of data is presented in a frequency table?** any data that can be counted

• **How can you use the frequency table to determine how many students were surveyed?** Add all the numbers in the Frequency column.

© Houghton Mifflin Harcourt

Do the Math

Skill ㉙

Use the frequency table at the right for Problems 1–3.

1. How many more players are on the football team than the basketball team?

   22 more players

2. Which team has the least number of players?

   basketball

3. How many players are on the hockey team?

   20 players

School Sports Teams	
Team	Frequency (Number of Players)
hockey	20
football	41
basketball	19
baseball	20

Use the frequency table below for Problems 4–6.

4. Is this statement true or false: "More people voted for drama than for comedy"?

   false

5. How many people voted in all?

   135 people

6. Which type of movie got 40 votes?

   action

Favorite Type of Movie	
Type of Movie	Frequency (Votes)
comedy	35
horror	27
drama	33
action	40

Check

7. Use the Movie frequency table above. Order the types of movie from the type with the greatest number of votes to the type with the least number of votes. Explain how you found the answer.

   action, comedy, drama, horror; First I ordered the
   number of votes from greatest to least, then I
   matched up the numbers with the types of movies.

Do the Math

Tell students to read the tables by reading across rows. Remind students that they need to correctly identify the number that goes with a category before comparing that category to others.

Talk Math

- **For Problem 1, how many players are on the football team?** 41 **How many are on the basketball team?** 19

- **For Problem 5, which four numbers should you add?** 35, 27, 33 and 40

Check

Guide students to see that they can order the numbers first, then find the corresponding types of movie.

Alternative Teaching Strategy

Interpreting a Frequency Table

Objective To read a frequency table and use it to answer simple questions

Materials sets of 4 index cards with *Wednesday*, *Friday*, *Monday*, and *Sunday* written on one card each

- Write this frequency table on the board:

Favorite Day to Do Laundry	
Day	**Frequency**
Wednesday	44
Friday	25
Monday	50
Sunday	61

- Explain that a number of people were asked which day they prefer to do laundry. The table shows the days chosen, and the frequency for each day.

- Place students in groups of 4. Instruct each student in a group to choose a day of the week card from a set.

- Ask students with *Sunday* cards to step forward. Ask: **How many people voted for Sunday?** 61 Guide students to line up *Sunday* in the first column with 61 in the second column, reading across the row.

- Next ask the students with a card for the day that got 50 votes to step forward.

- Then ask the student who got *6 fewer votes than Monday* to step forward. Ask: **How many votes did Monday get?** 50 **What is 6 less than 50?** 44 **Which day got 44 votes?** Wednesday

- Finally, direct students to stand up and arrange themselves in order (left to right) from the day that got the most votes to the day that got the least votes. Ask: **Which day got the fewest votes?** Friday

- Extend the activity by asking the students with cards for the days that fit the descriptions *got 11 more votes than Monday, twice as many votes as Friday, 19 more votes than Friday,* and so on, to raise their hands.

Response to Intervention • Tier 3   IIN58

Mean
Skill 30

Objective
To find the mean for a set of data using models and an algorithm.

Materials
connecting cubes

Vocabulary
mean The average of a set of numbers, found by dividing the sum of the numbers by the number of addends

Pre-Assess

Write this set of numbers on the board: 10, 3, 2, 5, 7, 3. Ask: **What operations would you use to find the mean?** addition and division Tell students to find the mean. 5

Common Misconception

• Students may incorrectly define mean as the middle number in an ordered set of data.

• To correct this, remind students that the mean is the average of the numbers. Give students the following example: 6, 8, 11, 12, 13. Direct them to see that the middle number is 11. Then use the algorithm to find the mean: 6 + 8 + 11 + 12 + 13 = 50, 50 ÷ 5 = 10. Guide them to see that the mean and middle number are not the same. Provide other examples as needed.

Learn the Math

The first problem on student page **IIN59** shows a way to use models to find the mean. Allow students to work through the problem with their own cubes. After modeling each number, students might rearrange the stacks in different ways. They may leave the stacks mostly intact and move cubes one at a time between stacks until all are identical. Some students may wish instead to take apart every stack and use the individual cubes to build entirely new, equal stacks.

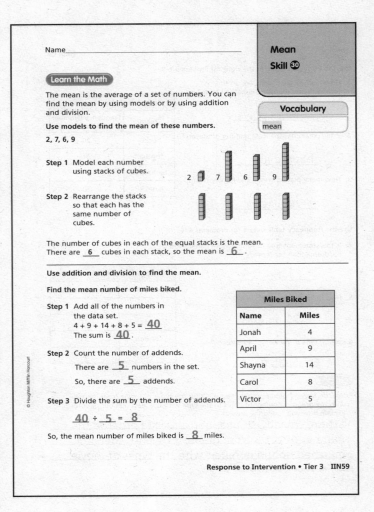

Guide students through using addition and division to find the mean of a set of numbers. The second problem shows a set of numbers as data in a table. Let students know that while they could model to find the mean, it can be quicker to use paper and pencil, especially when the numbers are greater.

Ask: **What are the numbers in this set of data?** 4, 9, 14, 8, 5 Tell students that the steps for finding the mean of a set of data remain the same no matter how the numbers are presented.

Talk Math

• **Is the order of numbers in a set of data important to finding the mean?** no

• **How would you use paper and a pencil to find the mean of the set of data in the first problem?** I would add all of the numbers, and divide the sum by 4, the number of addends.

Do the Math

Find the mean of each set of data.

1. 30, 40, 50, 36

_____39_____

2. 1, 3, 4, 4, 5, 1

_____3_____

3. 23, 12, 16, 19, 20

_____18_____

4. 10, 11, 8, 6, 5

_____8_____

5.

Distance Driven	
Day	Distance (in miles)
Monday	99
Tuesday	91
Wednesday	92
Thursday	94

mean = __94__ miles

6.

Baseball Games Attended	
Month	Number of Games
May	10
June	14
July	6
August	6
September	9

mean = __9__ games

Check

7. The snowfall for each day of a school week was: 3 inches, 1 inch, 1 inch, 7 inches and 3 inches. Lisa said that the mean snowfall could be found by adding 3 + 1 + 7 inches, and then dividing by 5. Was she correct? Explain.

Possible answer: Lisa was incorrect because she did not add all the numbers in the set of data. She should have added 3 + 1 + 1 + 7 + 3, then divided by the number of addends, 5.

Do the Math

Help students see that if they use models to find the mean, they can check the answer using addition and division. Ask students to write out all number sentences, rather than compute mentally. Remind them to count every addend to find the divisor.

Talk Math

- **How many numbers are in the set of data in Problem 2?** 6

- **If you use addition and division in Problem 4, what is the divisor?** 5

Check

Ask: **Did Lisa forget to include any addends?** yes
Ask: **What is the correct sum?** 3 + 1 + 1 + 7 + 3 = 15

Alternative Teaching Strategy

Find the Mean of a Set of Data

Objective To find the mean of a set of data using models.

Materials 28 1-inch blocks for each student

- Place students into small groups and hand out blocks. Write the following on the board: 6", 5", 8", 9". Tell students that these are the lengths of 4 different pencils (you may use pencil examples to show). Explain that they will work together to find the mean length of the pencils.

- Ask: **How could you model the length 8" using blocks?** line up or stack 8 1-inch blocks Tell students to line up blocks end to end to model 8". Instruct groups to model each of the lengths with the blocks.

- Write on the board: _mean length = average length._ Say: **The mean is the number of blocks that would be in each model if the models were equal in length.**

- Ask: **How many models are there?** 4 Ask groups to line up the models end to end. Ask: **What does this represent?** all of the lengths added together Write 6 + 5 + 8 + 9 on the board.

- Ask: **How would you make 4 identical models from this long line of blocks?** separate it into 4 equal pieces Write "÷ 4" on the board at the right.

- Instruct the groups to separate the long line of blocks into four equal groups. Ask: **How many blocks are in each of the 4 models?** 7 Write "= 7" on the board to complete the number sentence. Ask: **What is the mean?** 7"

- Tell students that they can find the mean of a set of numbers using a pencil and paper. Explain that they first add the numbers, then divide by the number of addends. Use the number sentence you wrote on the board for an example.

- Extend the activity by asking students to find the average length of these pencils: 3", 3", 4", 2" and 8". Ask them to first use models and then addition and division.

Response to Intervention • Tier 3   IIN60

Read a Pictograph
Skill ③

Objective
To read a pictograph where each symbol represents at least 2

Vocabulary
key The part of a graph that explains the symbol

pictograph A graph in which data is shown using pictures or symbols

Pre-Assess
Draw the following pictograph on the board:

Number of Aquarium Visitors	
Monday	🐟 🐟 🐟 🐟
Tuesday	🐟 🐟 🐟
Wednesday	🐟 🐟 🐟
Thursday	🐟 🐟 🐟 🐟
Friday	🐟 🐟 🐟 🐟 🐟

Key: Each 🐟 = 100 visitors.

Ask: Which day had the most visitors? Friday
How many visitors were there on Monday? 400
How many more visitors were there on Friday? 100

Common Misconception

• Students may not read a half-symbol correctly.

• To correct this, remind them that a half-symbol has half the value of a whole symbol. Ask them to find keys for pictographs that have half-symbols. Tell them to draw half-symbols below the keys and find their values by dividing the whole symbol values by 2.

Learn the Math

Tell students that a pictograph key gives the amount that each symbol represents. Direct them to the first pictograph on student page **IIN61**. Point out the common features of pictographs: two columns (one with symbols), a title and a key.

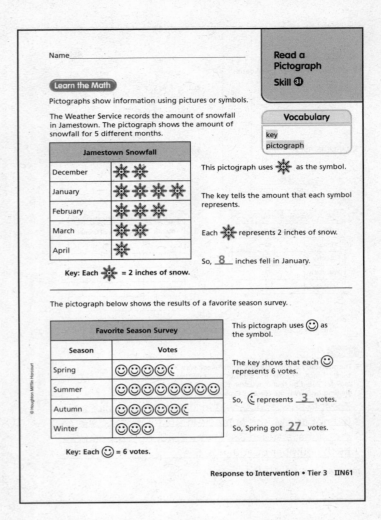

Ask: How many inches of snow does each symbol represent? 2 inches

For the second pictograph, guide students to see that they do not need to understand the key to find which season got the most or least votes. However, they do need to understand the key to count the votes for each season. Tell students that they can determine the number of votes for a season by counting the symbols in the row, then multiplying that number by the value shown in the key.

Help students understand the meaning of a half-symbol. Explain how to find the number of votes for Spring.

Talk Math

• **In the second pictograph, how many votes does a full smiley-face symbol represent?** 6 votes

• **How can you determine the number of votes that half of a smiley-face symbol represents?** Divide 6 by 2.

© Houghton Mifflin Harcourt

Use the Concert Attendance pictograph for Problems 1–3.

1. How many more people attended a concert on Saturday than Friday?

   <u>10 more people</u>

2. On which day did 60 people attend a concert?

   <u>Wednesday</u>

3. How many people attended on Thursday?

   <u>50 people</u>

Concert Attendance	
Tuesday	♫
Wednesday	♫♫♫
Thursday	♫♫♩
Friday	♫♫♫♩
Saturday	♫♫♫♫

Key: Each ♫ = 20 people.

Use the pictograph below for Problems 4–6.

4. What was the total number of people who were surveyed?

   <u>112 people</u>

5. Which snack got the fewest votes?

   <u>nuts</u>

6. How many votes did popcorn get?

   <u>32 votes</u>

Favorite Snack Survey	
Popcorn	♥♥♥♥
Apples	♥♥♥♥❤
Raisins	♥♥♥❤
Nuts	♥♥

Key: Each ♥ = 8 votes.

Check

7. Dave read the Favorite Snack Survey pictograph above, and said that popcorn and apples got the same number of votes. Is he correct? Explain.

   <u>No, he is not correct. Popcorn got 32 votes, and</u>
   <u>apples got 36 votes.</u>

IIN62   Response to Intervention • Tier 3

Skill 31

© Houghton Mifflin Harcourt

Do the Math

Have students look at student page **IIN62**. Review pictograph keys and the meaning of half-symbols. Remind students to read across a row to connect information in the first column with the number of symbols in the second column.

Talk Math

- **What does the key for the first pictograph tell you?** Each musical note symbol represents 20 people.

- **What does the key for the second pictograph tell you?** Each heart symbol represents 8 votes.

Check

Ask: **How many symbols are in the Apples row?** 4 and a half symbols. Ask: **What does a half symbol represent?** half the value of the whole symbol, 4 votes

---

Alternative Teaching Strategy

Interpret a Pictograph

Objective To read a pictograph in which each picture represents 2 or more

Materials sets of 8 index cards with the words *dolls, puzzles, blocks,* and *paint sets* each written on one card, and 30, 40, 50, or 20 each written on a card.

- Draw this pictograph on the board:

Number of Toys Sold	
Dolls	X X X X
Puzzles	X X X
Blocks	X X X X X
Paint sets	X X

Key: Each X = 10 toys.

- Place students into groups of 4. Tell them that they are going to work together to interpret the pictograph. Ask each student to choose one of the 4 cards with the toy type listed on it.

- Ask: **What different types of toys were sold?** dolls, puzzles, blocks, and paint sets **Guide** students to look at the key. Ask: **What does one X represent?** 10 toys

- Ask: **If one X is 10 toys, what does half an X represent?** half of 10 toys, 5 toys Ask: **Would two of the half-X symbols ever be in the same row? Why or why not?** No, because 2 half symbols are the same as 1 whole symbol.

- Ask: **How many paint sets were sold?** 20 paint sets Remind students to read across a row.

- Tell students to work together to determine how many of each type of toy was sold. Instruct students to pick up the number card that corresponds to their toy card.

- Afterwards, ask one group to explain how they found the number sold for each toy.

- Extend the activity by asking each student to list whether *more* or *less* of their type of toy was sold, compared to the other 3 types of toys.

© Houghton Mifflin Harcourt

Read a Bar Graph
Skill ③②

Objective
To read horizontal and vertical bar graphs with intervals of 2 or more

Materials
index cards

Vocabulary
bar graph A graph that shows data with vertical or horizontal bars

range The difference between the greatest and least numbers in a data set

Pre-Assess

Draw the following bar graph on the board:

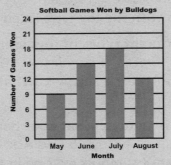

Ask: **How many games were won in June?** 15
What is the range of the number of games won? 9

Common Misconception

• Students may have trouble finding the value represented by a bar.

• To correct this, ask students to place the edge of an index card at the end of a bar, perpendicular to the scale. Instruct them to move along the straight edge to the scale to find the corresponding number. If the bar falls between two numbers, remind them to find a value halfway between the two numbers.

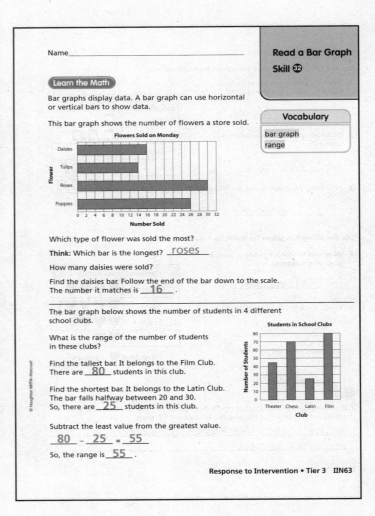

Learn the Math

Point out common features of all bar graphs using both graphs on student page **IIN63**: axis labels, a title and a scale.

Draw students attention to differences in vertical and horizontal bar graphs, namely the placement of scales and position of the bars. Ask students to find the intervals used on the scales. Remind students that different bar graphs will have different intervals.

Guide students through finding the range of values for the bar graph in the second problem. For extra practice, ask them to find the range of the numbers of flowers sold in the first problem. Also help students to compare groups within a graph. For example, they could compare the numbers of students in the Film and Theater clubs.

Talk Math

• **What is the interval for the first graph?** 2

• **Using the first graph, how would you determine how many more roses were sold than daisies?** I would find the number of roses sold, and subtract the number of daisies sold.

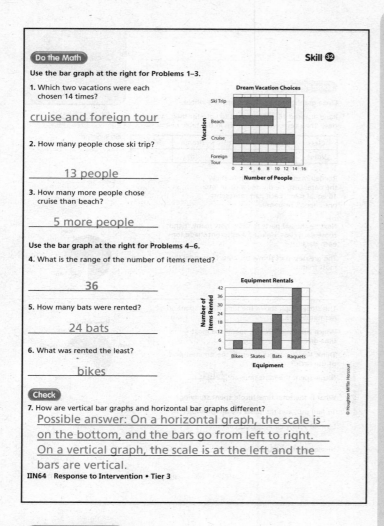

Use the bar graph at the right for Problems 1–3.

1. Which two vacations were each chosen 14 times?

<u>cruise and foreign tour</u>

2. How many people chose ski trip?

<u>13 people</u>

3. How many more people chose cruise than beach?

<u>5 more people</u>

Use the bar graph at the right for Problems 4–6.

4. What is the range of the number of items rented?

<u>36</u>

5. How many bats were rented?

<u>24 bats</u>

6. What was rented the least?

<u>bikes</u>

Check

7. How are vertical bar graphs and horizontal bar graphs different?

<u>Possible answer: On a horizontal graph, the scale is on the bottom, and the bars go from left to right. On a vertical graph, the scale is at the left and the bars are vertical.</u>

IIN64   Response to Intervention • Tier 3

Do the Math

Have students look at the graphs on student page **IIN64**. Remind them to note the intervals of a graph's scale. Guide them to see that a bar can be lined up with a number on the scale to determine its value, or a number on the scale can be used to find a specific bar.

Talk Math

• **For Problem 3, how many people chose a cruise vacation?** 14 **How many people chose a beach vacation?** 9

• **For Problem 6, what equipment has the shortest bar?** bikes

Check

Ask: **Where is the scale in a vertical bar graph? In a horizontal bar graph?** at the left side; on the bottom.

Alternative Teaching Strategy

Interpret a Bar Graph

Objective To read a bar graph with intervals equal to 2 or more

• Draw this bar graph on the board:

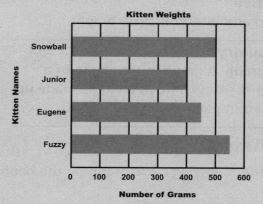

• Place students into four groups. Tell them that they are going to work together to interpret the horizontal bar graph.

• Ask: **What is the title of this bar graph?** Kitten Weights Guide students to look at the scale. Ask: **What are the labels on the scale?** 0, 100, 200, 300, 400, 500, 600 **What is the interval?** 100

• Ask: **What does each bar represent?** one kitten's weight **If a kitten weighed 300 grams, where would the bar extend to?** the 300 mark **If a kitten weighed 350 grams, where would the bar extend to?** halfway between the 300 and 400 marks

• Assign one kitten's name to each group. Tell students to work together to determine their kitten's weight, and how much more or less it weighs than the other kittens. Check answers together as a class.

• Next ask: **How much did the heaviest kitten weigh?** 550 grams **How much did the lightest kitten weigh?** 400 grams Write these values on the board.

• Guide students to find the range of kitten weights by subtracting the least weight from the greatest weight.

Objective
To read and interpret circle graphs

Vocabulary
circle graph A graph in the shape of a circle that shows data as a whole made up of different parts

Pre-Assess
Draw the following circle graph on the board:

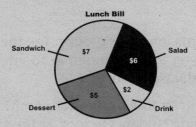

Lunch Bill

Ask: **What is the name of this type of graph?**
circle graph Ask: **How much did dessert cost?**
$5 **How many items were ordered for lunch?** 4
Which item was the most expensive? sandwich

Common Misconception

- When asked to compare one category to the whole data set, students may forget to include that category as part of the whole.

- To correct this, remind students that the full circle represents the whole data set, and all groups are needed to make up the whole circle, including the specific category they are comparing. Use the example above and point out that if they want to compare the amount spent on a sandwich to the total amount spent, they must add all the amounts spent, including the cost of a sandwich.

Learn the Math

Point out that the circle in a circle graph, represents the whole, or all the categories of the graph. Direct students to the circle graph in the first problem on student page **IIN65**, and use this to identify common features of circle graphs.

IIN65   Response to Intervention · Tier 3

Name_____

Learn the Math

Circle graphs show data as parts of a whole.

Randall asked 16 of his friends to vote for their favorite class. Their responses are shown in the table below.

Vocabulary

circle graph

Class	English	Art	Drama	Math
Votes	1	4	8	3

Randall made a circle graph to show the data. First, he divided a circle into 16 equal parts. Each part represents one friend's response.

Next he shaded parts to show how many friends chose each class. He used a different shade for each class.

The greatest part shows the class chosen by the most friends.

Favorite Class

This circle graph shows the time Nicole spent on her homework.

Which subject did Nicole spend the most time on?

Think: Which subject takes up the greatest part of the circle?

Nicole spent the most time on <u>Math</u>.

Homework Time

What is the total time Nicole spent studying?
To find out, add the times for all the subjects.

50 + 40 + 10 + 20 = <u>120</u> minutes

Nicole spent <u>120</u> minutes or <u>2</u> hours studying.

Use the second problem to help students interpret circle graphs. Guide them to compare categories by comparing the sizes of the corresponding parts of the circle.

Help students to add all parts together to get the value of the whole data set.

Talk Math

- **What is the title of the graph in the first problem? in the second problem?** Favorite Class; Homework Time

- **In the second graph, what does the whole circle represent?** the total time Nicole spent studying

- **Using the second graph, how would you find how much more time Nicole spent on Math than History?** Find the times for Math and History and subtract.

Do the Math

Skill 33

Use the circle graph at the right for Problems 1–3.

1. Who received the most votes?

   <u>Dahlia</u>

2. Who received the fewest votes?

   <u>Barbara</u>

3. Who received more votes than Bridget?

   <u>Dahlia</u>

Club President Election

Barbara 40 votes
105 votes — Dahlia
55 votes
Bridget

Use the circle graph below for Problems 4–6.

4. How many different types of art are in Tim's collection?

   <u>4 types of art</u>

5. Are there more drawings than photos in Tim's collection?

   <u>yes</u>

6. How many pieces of art are in Tim's collection?

   <u>36 pieces of art</u>

Tim's Art Collection

Photos 7
Sculptures 3
Paintings 16
Drawings 10

Check

7. Judi read the Art Collection circle graph. She said that paintings represent $\frac{1}{2}$ of Tim's art collection. Was she correct? Explain.

   <u>Possible answer: No. Paintings represent $\frac{16}{36} = \frac{4}{9}$ of</u>
   <u>Tim's art collection not $\frac{1}{2}$.</u>

Do the Math

For the problems on student page **IIN66**, remind students they can compare categories or groups by comparing the size of the corresponding parts on the graph. Guide students to add values of every group to get the value for the whole data set for Problem 6.

Talk Math

- **In Problem 2, which candidate has the smallest part of the circle?** Barbara

- **What are the groups shown in the Art Collection graph?** Photos, Drawings, Paintings and Sculptures

Check

Ask: **What is the total number of pieces of art?** 36 **What is half of 36?** 18

Alternative Teaching Strategy

Draw a Circle Graph

Objective To make a circle graph

Materials paper, pencil, ruler, colored pencils

- Tell students that some people were asked to vote for their favorite hot drink. Write the following on the board: Cocoa – 4 votes, Tea – 1 vote, Cider – 3 votes. Inform students that they will make a circle graph to show this information.

- Instruct each student to make a circle on a paper. Tell them that this represents the whole data set.

- Next explain that they will divide the circle into equal sections. Say: **The number of sections is equal to the number of people that voted.** Ask: **How many sections will there be?** 8 sections Guide students through partitioning the circle into 8 wedge-shaped parts.

- Say: **Now you will divide the sections into different categories. Each drink will be one category.** Ask: **How many categories are there?** 3 categories

- Ask: **How many people voted for tea?** 1 person **How many equal sections will be in the tea category?** 1 section Ask them to color in **1** section. Repeat the process for the other drinks, with different colors.

- Tell students to label each section, and to write a title. Show the finished graph:

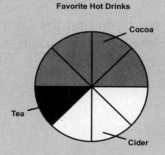

Favorite Hot Drinks

Cocoa
Tea
Cider

- Ask: **What fraction of the total votes did Cocoa get?** one-half Guide students to see that the Cocoa section represents half of the circle.

- Extend the activity by having students take their own surveys and represent the results in a circle graph.

Objective
To identify and model the properties of addition

Vocabulary
Associative Property of Addition The property states that you can group addends in different ways and still get the same sum

Commutative Property of Addition The property states that when the order of two addends is changed, the sum is the same

Identity Property of Addition (or Zero) The property states that the sum of any number and zero is that number

Pre-Assess
Write Identity (Zero) Property of Addition, Commutative Property of Addition and Associative Property of Addition on the board. Also write: $10 + 2 = 2 + 10$, $10 + 0 = 10$ and $10 + (2 + 5) = (10 + 2) + 5$. Ask students which property explains each equation. Instruct students to write two more equations for each property.

Common Misconception
- Students might confuse the Commutative and Associative Properties of Addition.

- To correct this, tell them that the <u>Commutative</u> Property says it does not matter which number <u>comes</u> first in an addition sentence.

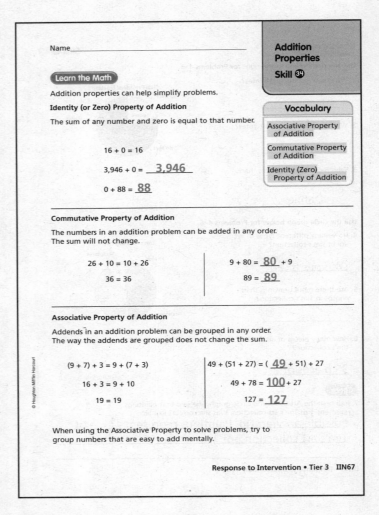

Help students see that the Associative Property can simplify addition problems since facts that are easy to add can be grouped together. Explain that adding 49 and 51 together first is a good choice since $49 + 51 = 100$. 100 is a number that is simple to work with. Let students know that they can use the Associative Property to change the grouping of addends to simplify the addition.

Talk Math
- **What does the Commutative Property state?** It states that the order in which addends are listed doesn't matter. The order of the addends does not affect the sum.

- **Why do you think the Identity Property is also called the Zero Property?** A number keeps its identity when zero is added to it.

Learn the Math
Go through each addition property on student page **IIN67** with the class.

For the Commutative Property, help students identify all of the addends in the problem. They need to make sure that there is the same number of addends on each side of the equal sign.

© Houghton Mifflin Harcourt

Do the Math

Find the missing number. Write which addition property you used.

1. $165 + \underline{0} = 165$

   Identity Property

2. $(44 + \underline{16}) + 2 = 44 + (16 + 2)$

   Associative Property

3. $(57 + 3) + 22 = 57 + (\underline{3} + 22)$

   Associative Property

4. $13 + 39 = 39 + \underline{13}$

   Commutative Property

5. $28 + (3 + 17) = (\underline{28} + 3) + 17$

   Associative Property

6. $1,399 + 0 = \underline{1,399}$

   Identity Property

7. $12 + (17 + \underline{18}) = (12 + 17) + 18$

   Associative Property

8. $\underline{11} + 0 = 11$

   Identity Property

9. $(17 + 6) + \underline{24} = 17 + (6 + 24)$

   Associative Property

10. $32 + \underline{14} = 14 + 32$

   Commutative Property

Check

11. How would you use the Associative Property to group these numbers so that you can add mentally? What is the sum?

$33 + 5 + 115$

I can group the numbers that end in 5 (115 and 5) first because they will add up to 120. This will give me a greater number that will be easier to add to 33. $33 + (5 + 115) = 33 + 120 = 153$

Do the Math

Guide students to identify all of the addends in the problems on student page **IIN68**. To help them distinguish between the Commutative and Associative Properties, ask: **Is the order of the numbers different, or is the grouping of the numbers different?**

Talk Math

- **What does the Associative Property state?** It states that I can group addends in various ways.

- **Which problems show this property?** Problems 2, 3, 5, 7, and 9

Check

Ask students which numbers they can most easily add mentally. Guide them to see that even if they can add 33 and 5 easily, it might be harder to add 38 and 115.

Alternative Teaching Strategy

Addition Properties

Objective To model the Properties of Addition

Materials sets of 12 index cards numbered 0 to 12, sets of 2 index cards labeled + and =, counters

- Have students work in groups. Hand out two sets of cards to each group of students.

- Write these properties on the board, with the examples:

   Identity (Zero) Property: $11 + 0 = 11$
   Commutative Property: $1 + 6 = 6 + 1$
   Associative Property: $2 + (3 + 10) = (2 + 3) + 10$

- Start with the Identity property. Have students model the example with index cards, and place counters under the cards.

$$\boxed{11} \quad + \quad \boxed{0} \quad = \quad \boxed{11}$$

   Then write: $3 + 0 = \underline{}$. Ask students to model the number sentence with index cards or counters. Ask: **What is the sum?** 3

- Next have students model the example of the Commutative Property with their index cards and counters, and find the sum on each side of the equation. Ask: **Does the order of the addends change the sum?** no Write: $\underline{} + 7 = 7 + 4$ on the board. **How can you use the Commutative Property to find the missing number?** I identify the addends on the right side, 7 and 4. Since the order of the addends does not affect the sum, I know the missing addend is 4.

- Now have the students look at the example of the Associative Property. Ask: **What do the parentheses mean?** They group addends to be added together first. Have them model the example and find the sum. **Do the different groupings affect the sum?** no Give students the example: $134 + 15 + 85$. **How could grouping make this addition problem easier?** I can group addends that are easy to add. Guide students to see that $134 + (15 + 85)$ may be simpler to add mentally.

- Have groups model and share additional problems.

Multiplication Properties
Skill 35

Pre-Assess
Write Zero Property, Identity Property, Commutative Property, and Associative Property on the board. Also write:
$10 \times 12 = 12 \times 10$, $12 \times 0 = 0$, $10 \times 1 = 10$ and $(10 \times 12) \times 3 = 10 \times (12 \times 3)$. Ask students which multiplication property corresponds to each equation. Challenge students to write two more equations to illustrate each property.

Common Misconception

• Students might confuse the multiplication properties.

• To correct this, have them write two or more examples of each. Also tell them that the Commutative Property refers to changing the order of two factors in an equation, and the Associative Property refers to changing the grouping when there are *three* or more factors.

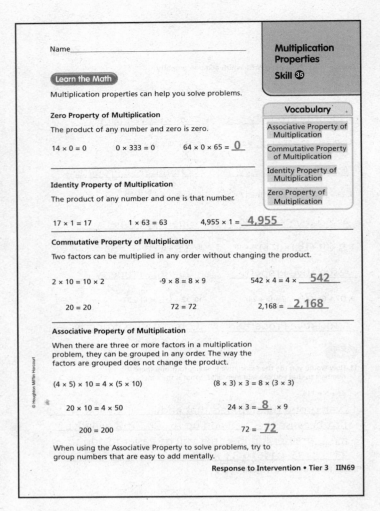

Learn the Math
Go through each property on student page **IIN69** with students. Explain that the Zero Property and the Identity Property can make solving problems easier.

Explain that if you see any string of factors multiplied by zero, you should know the product is zero. If you see any number multiplied by 1, you should know that the product is equal to that number.

Also guide the students to see that the Associative Property of Multiplication can simplify problems, since factors that are easy to compute mentally can be grouped together.

Talk Math

• **How can the Zero Property simplify multiplication problems with many factors?** It tells me that any number multiplied by zero is zero. Even if there are many factors in the problem, if zero is a factor the product will always be zero.

Do the Math

Skill **35**

Find the missing number. Write which multiplication property you used.

1. $12 \times \underline{1} = 12$

Identity Property

2. $15 \times \underline{3} = 3 \times 15$

Commutative Property

3. $3 \times 4 \times 8 \times 0 = \underline{0}$

Zero Property

4. $(1 \times 3) \times 12 = 1 \times (3 \times \underline{12})$

Associative Property

5. $7 \times 6 = \underline{6} \times 7$

Commutative Property

6. $199 \times 0 = \underline{0}$

Zero Property

7. $8 \times 4 = \underline{4} \times 8$

Commutative Property

8. $17 \times \underline{1} = 17$

Identity Property

9. $(4 \times 5) \times \underline{7} = 4 \times (5 \times 7)$

Associative Property

10. $\underline{14} \times 1 = 14$

Identity Property

11. $8 \times 7 = \underline{7} \times 8$

Commutative Property

12. $11 \times \underline{0} = 0$

Zero Property

Check

13. How would you use the Commutative Property to find an equivalent expression for 14×2? What is the product?

   The Commutative Property of Multiplication states that the order of factors can be changed without changing the product. The expression can be changed to 2×14. The product is 28.

IIN70   Response to Intervention • Tier 3

Do the Math

Guide students to identify all of the factors in the problems on student page **IIN70**. To help them distinguish between the Commutative and Associative Properties, ask: **Is the order of the numbers different, or is the grouping of the numbers different?**

Talk Math

- **What does the Associative Property tell you?** Grouping in different ways will not affect the product.

- **What does the Identity Property tell you?** The product of any number multiplied by one is that number.

Check

Ask students to explain the Commutative Property. Guide them to identify and rearrange the factors.

Alternative Teaching Strategy

Modeling Properties with Arrays

Objective To model multiplication properties (Zero, Identity, Commutative, Associative)

Materials grid paper

- Write these properties on the board, with examples:

  Identity Property: $9 \times 1 = 9$
  Commutative Property: $4 \times 6 = 6 \times 4$
  Associative Property: $(2 \times 3) \times 4 = 2 \times (3 \times 4)$
  Zero Property: $7 \times 0 = 0$

- Start with the example for the Identity Property. Ask: **What are the factors?** 9 and 1 Have students draw an array that shows 9×1. **What is the product?** 9 Guide them to see that when 9 is multiplied by 1, the product is 9.

- Move on to the Commutative Property. Have students draw an array that models 4×6. Ask: **What is the product?** 24 Have students draw an array for 6×4. **Is this product the same as the product for 4×6?** yes **Did the order of the factors change the product?** no

- Now have the students look at the example for the Associative Property. Ask: **What do the parentheses mean?** The parentheses group factors to be multiplied first. Have half of the students or groups model $(2 \times 3) \times 4$ by drawing a 2 by 3 array four times. Have the others model $2 \times (3 \times 4)$ by drawing a 3 by 4 array two times. Let all of the groups find and report the product. **Does the grouping affect the product?** no

- Finally, have students model the Zero Property with $7 \times 0 = 0$. Help them think of ideas for modeling zero, such as a blank piece of paper or an empty grid, seven times. Ask: **What is the product of a number and zero?** 0

Expressions
Skill 36

Objective
To write and evaluate addition and subtraction expressions

Materials
10 pencils

Vocabulary
expression A part of an equation that has numbers and operation signs but does not have an equal sign

variable A letter or symbol that stands for one or more numbers

Pre-Assess
Write two expressions on the board, such as 10 − 3 and 7 + p. Hold 10 pencils and say: **I have ten pencils.** Give three pencils away to nearby students and say: **I give three out to students.** Ask: **What operation describes what happened to my pencils?** subtraction **Which expression shows what I did with the pencils?** 10 − 3

Hold up the seven pencils. Say: **I have 7 pencils.** Ask: **What if someone gives me some more pencils? What expression can you write to show this?** Possible answer: 7 + p Ask students to evaluate the expression if p = 2. 9

Common Misconception
- Students may find it difficult to determine which item to represent with a variable.

- Explain that a variable represents a number that is not known. When they read word problems, they should look for items that are not given an exact value, but are described as "some," "a few," or with similar terms.

Learn the Math

Read the definitions for *expression* and *variable*. Tell students that a variable is a letter or symbol that stands for an unknown number. Tell them

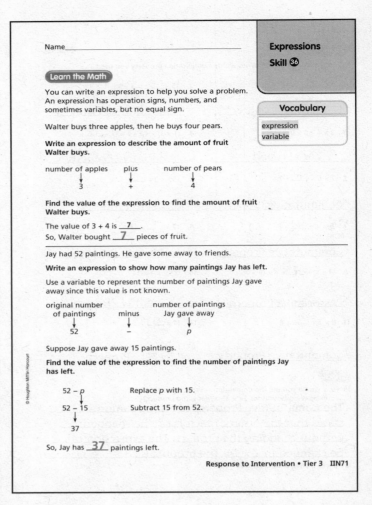

that they can use any letter for a variable, but that it may be easiest to choose a letter with a meaning, such as *p* for paintings. To find the value of an expression with a variable, they should replace the variable with the given value.

Guide students through each example on student page **IIN71**.

Ask them to pick out key words or phrases that suggest addition or subtraction. It is important to understand the meaning of the words before attempting to write an expression.

In the last example, have students point to the words that identify the 15 and the variable.

Talk Math

- **How do you write an unknown value in an expression?** You use a variable.

- **What do you need to know to evaluate an expression?** The value of all of the terms, including the variable.

Do the Math

Skill 36

Write an expression to match the words.

1. Rosie has 12 pairs of socks. She buys 8 more pairs.

    _____ 12 + 8 _____

2. Simon had 13 library books. He returned 7 to the library.

    _____ 13 – 7 _____

Write an expression with a variable. Tell what the variable represents.

3. A girl had a bunch of balloons. Two of the balloons popped.

    _b_ – 2, the variable represents the original number of balloons

4. Jillian ate 9 dried apricots and some raisins.

    9 + _r_, the variable represents the number of raisins

Find the value of the expression. Show your work.

5. $33 - t$ if $t = 17$

    _____ 33 – 17 _____
    _____ 16 _____

6. $100 + g$ if $g = 101$

    _____ 100 + 101 _____
    _____ 201 _____

7. $103 - b$ if $b = 23$

    _____ 103 – 23 _____
    _____ 80 _____

8. $13 + f$ if $f = 100$

    _____ 13 + 100 _____
    _____ 113 _____

Check

9. Georgia baked 5 pies and gave a few away. The expression $5 - p$ shows how many pies she has left. What is the variable in this expression? What does the variable represent?

    The variable is _p_. It represents the number of pies that Georgia gave away.

Do the Math

Help students work through student page **IIN72**. In Problem 3, the variable is the minuend and not the subtrahend. Explain that a variable can stand for any term in an expression.

Talk Math

- **In Problem 2, what operation corresponds to returning the library books?** subtraction

- **In Problem 4, how do you know whether the variable should represent apricots or raisins?** It represents raisins because the number of raisins is unknown.

Check

Have students circle the terms in the expression and draw an arrow to the parts of the sentence to which they correspond. Guide them to see that the variable is an unknown value described as "a few."

Alternative Teaching Strategy

Write and Evaluate Expressions

Objective To write and evaluate addition and subtraction expressions

Materials notebook paper or any common classroom objects

- Write the following problem on the board: "A student had 3 sheets of notebook paper. He was given 6 more sheets." Ask students to act out the situation.

- Write an addition expression to describe the situation. Ask: **How many sheets did he start with?** 3 Write this under "a student has 3 sheets." **What operation represents being given the paper?** addition Then write an addition symbol under "He was given." **How many did he get?** 6 Write this under "6 more". Have a student read the expression 3 + 6.

- Ask: **What is the value of the expression 3 + 6?** 9 **What does it show?** The pages he has now.

- Next replace "3 sheets" with "some sheets" and erase the 3 from the number sentence. Explain that you now don't know how many sheets he started with. Ask: **What can represent an unknown value?** a variable Explain to students that a variable is a letter or symbol. Write the variable *s* in the expression.

- Say: **Suppose *s* is equal to 18. What is the value of the expression?** 24 Have students evaluate the expression for different values of *s*.

- Repeat the activity using the original problem, replacing "He was given 6 more" with "He recycled 2." Guide the students to write the subtraction expression that represents the new problem. 3 – 2

Number Patterns
Skill ③⑦

Objective
To identify, complete and extend number patterns

Pre-Assess
Write this simple pattern on the board: 4, 8, 16, 32, 64. Ask: **What rule describes this number pattern?** multiply by 2 Have students extend the pattern by three numbers. 128, 256, 512 Then, ask students to write a new pattern following the same rule, starting with the number 10. 10, 20, 40, 80, 160

Common Misconception
- Students may predict and apply a rule without testing it, or without testing it on more than the first two numbers in the pattern.

- To correct this, tell students that some rules that work for the first two numbers in the pattern will not work for the other numbers. Because of this, they must test possible rules on all given numbers in a pattern.

Learn the Math
Read the pattern in the first problem on student page **IIN73** to the class. Ask whether the numbers increase or decrease. Point out that when the numbers in a pattern increase, the rule for the pattern will involve addition or multiplication. Conversely, when the numbers in a pattern decrease, the rule will involve subtraction or division.

Remind students that every rule must be tested on all the given numbers in a pattern. The first problem shows a possible rule for a pattern that does not work on all numbers.

The first problem shows the basic method for finding missing numbers in patterns and for extending patterns. First, a rule must be found and tested, then the rule is applied to find missing numbers.

IIN73   Response to Intervention • Tier 3

Name_____

Number Patterns
Skill ③⑦

Learn the Math
Number patterns can be explained by rules.

Write a rule for the pattern. Then find the missing numbers in the pattern.

3, 6, 9, 12, 15, ☐, ☐, 24

Step 1 Find a rule.   **Think:** What rule changes 3 to 6? Try *multiply by 2.*
Test the rule: $3 \times 2 = 6$; $6 \times 2 = \underline{12}$, $6 \times 2 \neq 9$
The rule *multiply by 2* does not work.

Try another rule.   **Think:** What other rule changes 3 to 6? Try *add 3.*
Test the rule:
3, 6, 9, 12, 15, ☐, ☐, 24   (+3 each)
The rule *add 3* works.

Step 2 Use the rule to find the missing numbers. $15 + 3 = \underline{18}$ $18 + 3 = \underline{21}$

So, the missing numbers are $\underline{18}$ and $\underline{21}$.

Some rules have more than one operation. Try two operations to find a rule for a pattern in which numbers decrease and then increase.

14, 10, 20, 16, 32, ☐, ☐   (−4, ×2 alternating)

The rule for this pattern is *subtract 4, multiply by 2.*

Use the rule to extend the pattern.
$32 - 4 = \underline{28}$ $28 \times 2 = \underline{56}$

So, the next two numbers are $\underline{28}$ and $\underline{56}$.

Response to Intervention • Tier 3   IIN73

© Houghton Mifflin Harcourt

The second problem shows a rule that has more than one operation. The numbers in this particular pattern alternate between decreasing and increasing. Tell students there may also be patterns in which the second number is greater than the first, and the numbers alternate between increasing and decreasing.

Remind students that a rule can use any operation.

Talk Math

- **Is there another rule that could explain the first three numbers in the second pattern?** subtract 4, add 10

- **Does this rule work for all of the numbers in the pattern?** no, 32 is not equal to 16 + 10

© Houghton Mifflin Harcourt

Write a rule to explain the pattern.

1. 2500, 500, 100, 20, 4

2. 1, 15, 29, 43, 57

___divide by 5___

___add 14___

Write a rule to explain the pattern.
Use the rule to find the missing numbers.

3. 72, 63, ☐, 45, 36, 27, ☐

4. 5, 10, 20, ☐, 80, ☐

___subtract 9; the___
___missing numbers___
___are 54 and 18___

___multiply by 2; the___
___missing numbers___
___are 40 and 160___

5. 9, 6, 13, 10, 17, ☐ ☐

6. 11, 14, 7, 10, 5, ☐ ☐

___subtract 3, add 7;___
___the next numbers___
___are 14 and 21___

___add 3, divide by 2;___
___the next numbers___
___are 8 and 4.___

Check

7. Can the pattern below be explained by either the rule
multiply by 4 or the rule *add 12*? Why or why not.

4, 16, 28, 40, 52, 64

___No. Possible response: the rule *add 12* works for all___
___of the numbers, but *multiply by 4* only works for the___
___first two numbers.___

Do the Math

Have students look at student page **IIN74**. Ask students to identify all possible rules that fit the first two or three numbers in each pattern, and then to test each rule on all the numbers in that pattern. Tell students that patterns which alternate between increasing and decreasing numbers may have rules with two operations.

Talk Math

- **What possible rules could fit the first two numbers in the pattern in Problem 1?** Possible answers: divide by 5, or subtract 2,000

- **Which rule fits all the numbers?** divide by 5

Check

Guide students to test both possible rules. The rule *multiply by 4* will not work past the second number in the pattern, so students can stop the test at that point.

Alternative Teaching Strategy

Find and Use Rules for Number Patterns

Objective To identify and extend number patterns

Materials square tiles, sets of 4 index cards on which the following is written: 10, add 10; 33, subtract 4; 3, multiply by 3; 100, divide by 5.

- Write the following pattern on the board:

  4, 8, 12, 16, 20. Ask students to model the numbers using tiles, then draw the picture on the board:

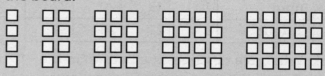

- Ask: **What is the difference between the first and the second sections?** 4 tiles **What two rules could you apply to the first section to get the second?** add 4, or multiply by 2

- Tell students to test each rule on the next section. Ask: **Is the third section equal to the second section multiplied by 2?** no Guide students to see that *add 4* works for all of the numbers. Say: **Add 4 is the rule for the pattern.**

- Place students in pairs. Give two of the index cards to each student in the pair, and instruct them to keep their cards hidden. Say: **The number is the first number in a pattern, the rule is the pattern rule.**

- Have one student make a four-number pattern using the guidelines on one card. To do this, guide students to apply the rule to the number on the card. Continue applying the rule until there are four numbers.

- Tell students to show the pattern to their partner. Instruct the partner to find the rule for the pattern. Partners should switch roles until each has written two patterns and found two rules.

Patterns and Functions
Skill ⓷⓼

Objective
To identify patterns and rules in function tables

Pre-Assess

Draw this table on the board.

Input	1	13	20	22
Output	9	21	28	30

Ask: **What rule describes the pattern in the table?** The rule is *add eight.* Give students additional input numbers and direct them to find the output using the rule.

Common Misconception

• Students may try to find a rule by comparing one input number to another, rather than comparing input to output.

• To correct this, explain that the rule for the table describes how the input number is related to output. Tell them that for every input there is just one output.

Go through the problem on student page **IIN75** with the class. Ask students to say each input/output pair: **input 5, output 25.** Introduce the idea that an increase or decrease from input to output reveals the type of operation the rule may use. Be sure that students understand that they are comparing input to output for each pair, rather than seeing whether input values increase or decrease. Direct students to look at the first pair of numbers.

Name_____

Patterns and Functions
Skill ⓷⓼

Learn the Math

You can look for patterns to find the rule for an input/output table. You can use the rule to find missing numbers in the table.

Find a rule for the table below.

Input	5	7	8	9	10	11
Output	25	35	40	45	50	55

Step 1 Look at the first pair of numbers.
How are 5 and 25 related?

Think: 5 + 20 = 25 So the rule could be *add 20.*

Step 2 Look at the second pair of numbers.

Test the rule *add 20* on 7 and 35.

Think: 7 + 20 ≠ 35 So the rule does not work.

Step 3 If the rule does not work, look back at the first pair of numbers.
How else could 5 and 25 be related?

Think: 5 × 5 = 25 So the rule could be *multiply by 5.*

Step 4 Test the rule *multiply by 5* on other pairs of numbers.

7 × 5 = 35   8 × 5 = 40   9 × 5 = __45__

Does it work? __yes__

So, the rule is __multiply by 5__ .

Use the rule to find the missing numbers in the table.

10 × 5 = __50__   11 × 5 = __55__

So, the missing numbers in the table are __50__ and __55__ .

Response to Intervention • Tier 3   IIN75

• **Does the output increase or decrease from the input?** It increases.

• **What type of operations could cause the output to increase?** addition or multiplication

• **Why is *add 20* not the rule?** It doesn't work on all the input/output pairs.

Remind students that a rule must work on every input/output pair in the table. Guide them to always test potential rules on all the given pairs of numbers.

Lead students through using a rule to find missing numbers in a function table. Guide them to see that they need a rule and an input number to find an output number. Ask: **How can you find missing output numbers in a table?** Use the rule. Apply the rule to the input number to find the output.

© Houghton Mifflin Harcourt

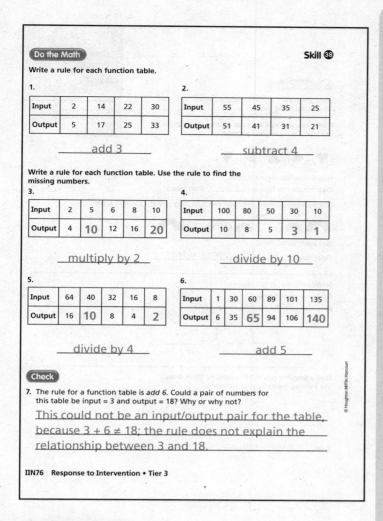

Do the Math — Skill 38

Write a rule for each function table.

1.

Input	2	14	22	30
Output	5	17	25	33

add 3

2.

Input	55	45	35	25
Output	51	41	31	21

subtract 4

Write a rule for each function table. Use the rule to find the missing numbers.

3.

Input	2	5	6	8	10
Output	4	10	12	16	20

multiply by 2

4.

Input	100	80	50	30	10
Output	10	8	5	3	1

divide by 10

5.

Input	64	40	32	16	8
Output	16	10	8	4	2

divide by 4

6.

Input	1	30	60	89	101	135
Output	6	35	65	94	106	140

add 5

Check

7. The rule for a function table is *add 6*. Could a pair of numbers for this table be input = 3 and output = 18? Why or why not?

This could not be an input/output pair for the table, because 3 + 6 ≠ 18; the rule does not explain the relationship between 3 and 18.

IIN76   Response to Intervention • Tier 3

Do the Math

Have students look at student page **IIN76**. Remind students to examine input/output pairs. Emphasize that it is not important whether there is a pattern to the input numbers (as there is in Problem 2), or to the output numbers. Look for a rule that describes how each input is changed to become the output.

Talk Math

- **In Problem 2, is the output greater or less than the input?** less than

- **Which operations might be in a rule if the output is less than the input?** subtraction or division

Check

Ask: **What is the sum of 3 and 6?** 9 **Is this equal to the output number?** no

---

Alternative Teaching Strategy

Make Function Tables

Objective To use a rule to make a function table

Materials number cubes

- Give two number cubes to each student or group. Write a blank function table with an input column and an output column on the board, and instruct the students to copy it. Also write *Rule: Multiply by 2.*

- Tell students that they are going to make an input/output table. First, they will use the number cubes to randomly select numbers for the input column. Say: **For each toss, add the values together and write the number in the input column.** For example, if they toss two 6s, the input is 12.

- Tell students they will next fill the output column. Explain that output and input are related by the rule. Ask: **What is the rule?** multiply by 2 Show students how to find the output. In the table on the board, write 8 in the input column. **What is 8 multiplied by 2?** 16 Write this in the output column.

- Direct students to apply the rule to each input to find all the values for the output column. Ask students to share their completed tables with the class.

- Ask: **How is an output related to an input?** by the rule **Are the inputs related to one another?** No, they are randomly selected.

- Afterwards, show the class function tables with various rules. For each, tell students to predict rules for the first input/output pair. Write these predictions on the board. Then instruct them to test these rules on every pair. Ask: **Did the rule work for the table? Why or why not?** Guide them to see that a rule must fit every input/output pair.

Geometric Patterns

Skill ③⑨

Objective
To identify and extend geometric patterns

Materials
tracing paper

Vocabulary
pattern unit The part of a pattern that repeats

Pre-Assess
Show students the following patterns:

Ask them to write a rule for each, then copy and draw the next figure in each pattern. Rule for top pattern: black, black, white. Rule for bottom pattern: Increase the number of small circles by 1 after each donut.

Common Misconception
- Some students may not recognize the rule for a pattern that does not repeat.
- To correct this, remind students that geometric patterns can be just like number patterns where they continue to add something to the previous figure.

Learn the Math

Tell students that patterns made of repeating objects or figures are geometric patterns. Like number patterns, geometric patterns follow rules.

Two types of geometric patterns are shown in the lesson, simple repeating patterns and expanding patterns. Take students through the patterns on student page **IIN77**. Encourage students to model

---

Name_____

Geometric Patterns

Skill ③⑨

Vocabulary
pattern unit

Learn the Math

Some geometric patterns have a pattern unit that repeats over and over.

Find a possible rule for each pattern. Then draw the next figure in your pattern.

Notice how the figure rotates.

Rule: rotate the figure ___90___°, then repeat.

Some patterns have more than one rule. This pattern has two rules:

Size rule: large, small

Color rule: _____black, gray, white_____

_____

Some patterns do not repeat.
Draw the next figure.
Rule: Increase the number of sides by 1.

?

Find a possible rule for the pattern. Then draw the missing figure in your pattern.

?

Rule: _triangle, square, circle, repeat_

Response to Intervention • Tier 3   IIN77

© Houghton Mifflin Harcourt

---

the first pattern using tracing paper. Remind students how to rotate a figure 90°. It is the same as $\frac{1}{4}$ turn.

For the second problem, draw attention to the fact that more than one rule is needed to describe the pattern.

For the third pattern, guide students to test the rule *increase number of sides by one*. Count the number of sides in each consecutive figure.

Talk Math

- **How are the first and second patterns the same?** They both repeat.
- **How are the patterns different?** The figures in the first pattern are in different positions; they are rotated 90° each time. The figures in the second pattern are always in the same position.

© Houghton Mifflin Harcourt

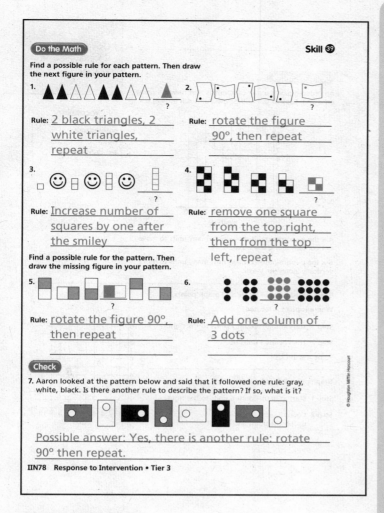

Do the Math

Skill **39**

Find a possible rule for each pattern. Then draw the next figure in your pattern.

1. ▲▲△△▲▲△△ ▲ ?

Rule: 2 black triangles, 2 white triangles, repeat

2. [figures] ?

Rule: rotate the figure 90°, then repeat

3. ☐☺☐☺☐☺☐ ?

Rule: Increase number of squares by one after the smiley

4. [checkered squares] ?

Rule: remove one square from the top right, then from the top left, repeat

Find a possible rule for the pattern. Then draw the missing figure in your pattern.

5. [squares] ?

Rule: rotate the figure 90°, then repeat

6. [dot patterns] ?

Rule: Add one column of 3 dots

Check

7. Aaron looked at the pattern below and said that it followed one rule: gray, white, black. Is there another rule to describe the pattern? If so, what is it?

[pattern of rectangles with circles]

Possible answer: Yes, there is another rule: rotate 90° then repeat.

IIN78 Response to Intervention • Tier 3

Do the Math

Guide students to find the rules in Problems 1 and 2 on student page **IIN78**. Remind students that rules can be about position, size, shape or color. For Problems 3 and 4, ask students to note if any figure is added or taken away from the pattern shown.

Talk Math

- **In Problem 2, how is the second figure different from the first?** It is in a different position.

- **In Problem 4, how are the small squares changed in the pattern?** A square is removed from the top right, then from the top left, then from the top right.

Check

Ask: **If the second figure was the same color as the first, would it be identical?** no Ask: **How is it different?** It is rotated 90°.

Alternative Teaching Strategy

Make Geometric Patterns

Objective To use rules to make geometric patterns

Materials 15 congruent figures of each shape including trapezoids, squares, circles, triangles, and stars for each group

- Distribute geometric figures to pairs or small groups. Explain that they will make geometric patterns with figures, following particular pattern rules. First, have students start a pattern by placing a trapezoid on a work surface, long base at the bottom.

- Say: **The rule for this first pattern is *rotate 180°.*** Write this on the board. Ask: **What does it mean to rotate a figure 180°?** Turn it $\frac{1}{2}$ turn.

- Direct students to place a second trapezoid to the right of the first, rotated 180°. Ask: **In what position should you place the next trapezoid in the pattern?** It will be rotated 180° from the second trapezoid, so it will look like the first. Guide students to extend the pattern to 8 or 10 figures. Draw the finished pattern on the board, under the rule.

- Ask students to clear the work space, then start a new pattern by making a column of squares, two high.

- Say: **The rule for this next pattern is *increase the number of squares in a column by 1.*** Write this on the board.

- Guide students to place a column of three squares to the right of the first column.

- Ask: **How many squares should be in the next column?** 4 **How do you know this?** It is 1 more than the previous column.

- Tell students to keep putting columns of squares into their pattern, until they run out of squares. Draw the finished pattern on the board, under the rule.

Response to Intervention • Tier 3   IIN78

Objective
To identify, locate, and graph points on a coordinate grid

Materials
grid paper

Vocabulary
coordinate grid A grid formed by a horizontal number line, the *x*-axis, and a vertical number line, the *y*-axis

ordered pair A pair of numbers that are used to locate a point on a coordinate grid

x-axis The horizontal number line on a coordinate grid

x-coordinate The first number in an ordered pair; it tells the distance to move horizontally

y-axis The vertical number line on a coordinate grid

y-coordinate The second number in an ordered pair; it tells the distance to move vertically

Pre-Assess

Instruct students to draw a 10-by-10 coordinate grid on grid paper, and to label the *x*- and *y*-axes. Show students a list of ordered pairs: (1,3), (2,5), (0,4), (6,3). Ask students to graph and label each point on the coordinate grid. For one ordered pair, ask students to identify the *x*-coordinate and the *y*-coordinate.

Common Misconception

• Students may confuse the *x*-coordinate and *y*-coordinate in an ordered pair.

• To correct this, explain that the *x*-coordinate is always given first. For some students, it may help to remember that *x* comes before *y* in the alphabet, like the *x*-coordinate comes before the *y*-coordinate in an ordered pair.

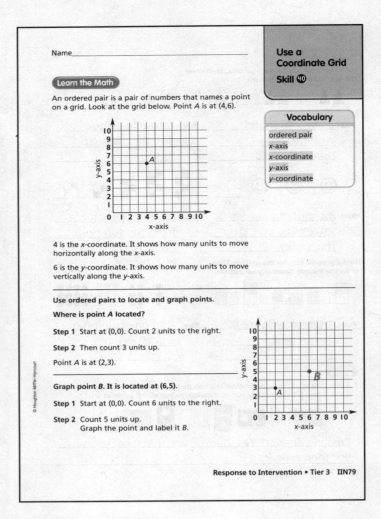

Learn the Math

Have students look at the coordinate grid on student page IIN79 and discuss its different parts.

Talk about ordered pairs. Explain that each ordered pair has only one *x*-coordinate and one *y*-coordinate, and that the *x*-coordinate is always listed first. Encourage students to first move along the *x*-axis, then along the *y*-axis, when finding coordinates on a grid.

Tell students that points on coordinate grids may be labeled different ways. They could have letter labels, as in the examples, or they may be labeled with the ordered pair. Explain that coordinate grids can be also used to make maps and find locations in real life.

Talk Math

• **Along which axis do you first move when graphing a point?** the *x*-axis

• **What is the name of the vertical axis?** *y*-axis

© Houghton Mifflin Harcourt

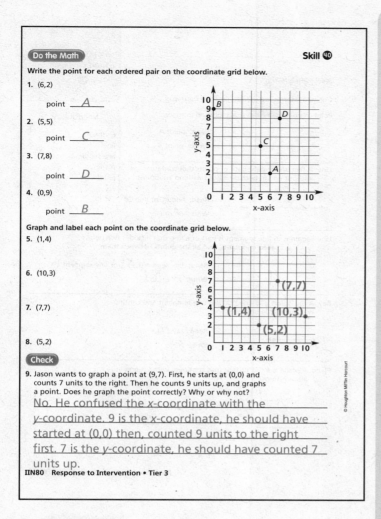

Do the Math Skill ④⓪

Write the point for each ordered pair on the coordinate grid below.

1. (6,2)

   point ___A___

2. (5,5)

   point ___C___

3. (7,8)

   point ___D___

4. (0,9)

   point ___B___

Graph and label each point on the coordinate grid below.

5. (1,4)

6. (10,3)

7. (7,7)

8. (5,2)

Check

9. Jason wants to graph a point at (9,7). First, he starts at (0,0) and counts 7 units to the right. Then he counts 9 units up, and graphs a point. Does he graph the point correctly? Why or why not?

   No. He confused the x-coordinate with the y-coordinate. 9 is the x-coordinate, he should have started at (0,0) then, counted 9 units to the right first. 7 is the y-coordinate, he should have counted 7 units up.

IIN80 Response to Intervention • Tier 3

Alternative Teaching Strategy

Make a Coordinate Grid Map

Objective To locate and graph points on a coordinate grid

Materials grid paper, colored pencils

• Tell students that you are going to create a map using a coordinate grid. Ask each student to draw a 10-by-10 coordinate grid, and to label the *x*- and *y*-axes. Draw an example on the board.

• Write (5,7) on the board. Ask: **What is this called?** an ordered pair Ask students to identify the *x*-coordinate, 5, and the *y*-coordinate, 7. Ask: **How do you use this ordered pair to graph a point on the grid?** Start at (0,0) move 5 units to the right. Then move 7 units up and graph a point. Guide students through the process.

• Write on the board: (5,1), (5,10). Instruct students to graph these points, then ask them to draw a line through the points. Say: **This represents 1ˢᵗ Avenue.**

• Write on the board: (2,7), (9,7). Instruct students to graph these points, and to draw a line through them. Say: **This line represents 7ᵗʰ Street.** Ask: **Where is the intersection of 1ˢᵗ Avenue and 7ᵗʰ Street?** point (5,7)

• Write these coordinates and labels on the board: Bank (4,2); Coffee Shop (4,3); School (2,5); Police Station (3,9); Hospital (7,5). Ask the students to graph and label the points using colored pencils.

• Students then pair up with partners. One partner gives an ordered pair and a label, such as (8,1): Joe's house. The other partner graphs and labels this on their coordinate grid. Once they have filled maps in with 5 or more points (or additional streets), ask the students to share them with the class.

Do the Math

Have students look at student page IIN80. Remind students that the *x*-coordinate is listed first in an ordered pair. Explain that any number along the number lines of the *x*-axis and *y*-axis can be part of an ordered pair, including 0.

Talk Math

• In Problem 5, what is the *x*-coordinate? 1

• How do you find this *x*-coordinate position on the coordinate grid? Start at 0 on the *x*-axis and move right 1.

Check

What is the *x*-coordinate? 9 What is the *y*-coordinate? 7 Guide students to see that Jason should have moved 9 units to the right, and 7 units up.

Objective
To identify points, line segments, endpoints, lines, rays, and planes

Materials
ruler or straight-edge, string

Vocabulary
endpoint The point at either end of a line segment or at the starting point of a ray

line A straight path of points in a plane that continues without end in both directions with no endpoints

line segment A part of a line that includes two points called endpoints and all the points between them

plane A flat surface that continues without end in all directions

point An exact location in space

ray A part of a line that has one endpoint and continues without end in one direction

Pre-Assess
Ask students to draw and label examples of: $\overline{AB}$, $\overrightarrow{JK}$, $\overleftrightarrow{LM}$, plane *XYZ*, and point *X*. Ask: **How many endpoints does a line segment have?** two **How many endpoints does a ray have?** one **Does a line have endpoints?** no

Common Misconception
• Students many confuse the terms *ray* and *line segment*.

• To correct this, remind students that both are parts of a line, but a ray continues without end in one direction. For some students it may help to remember that *line segment* is two words, and a line segment has two endpoints. *Ray* is one word, and a ray has only one endpoint.

Learn the Math
Tell students that geometric terms are used when describing plane and solid figures.

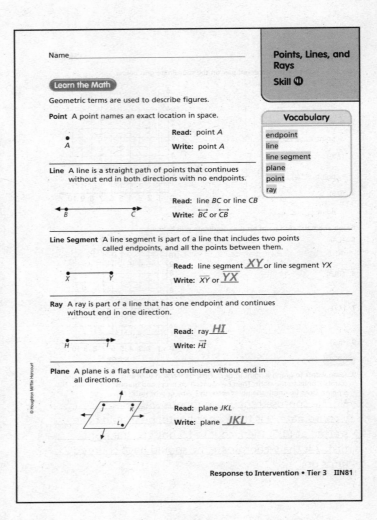

Go through each geometric term on student page **IIN81**. Ask: **How do you say the name of the point?** point *A* Show students the arrows on each end of the line. Explain that these indicate the line extends in both directions.

Ask students to circle the endpoints on the line segment and the ray. Point out that while the points used to name lines and line segments can be given in any order, when naming rays the endpoint is always given first. Assist students in drawing line segments and rays.

Have students identify real-world examples of each of the figures shown. Some examples include a table top models a plane or a piece of string models a line segment.

Talk Math
• **Does a line have endpoints?** no

• **What is the difference between a line and a ray?** A line is a straight path in a plane that continues without end in both directions. A ray is part of a line. It has one endpoint and continues without end in one direction.

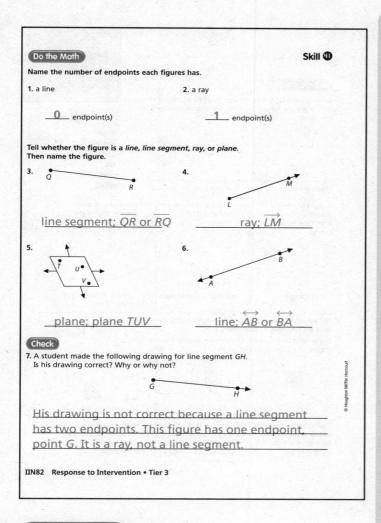

Do the Math Skill ④

Name the number of endpoints each figures has.

1. a line

___0___ endpoint(s)

2. a ray

___1___ endpoint(s)

Tell whether the figure is a *line, line segment, ray,* or *plane.*
Then name the figure.

3.

line segment; $\overline{QR}$ or $\overline{RQ}$

4.

ray; $\overrightarrow{LM}$

5.

plane; plane *TUV*

6.

line; $\overleftrightarrow{AB}$ or $\overleftrightarrow{BA}$

Check

7. A student made the following drawing for line segment *GH.*
Is his drawing correct? Why or why not?

His drawing is not correct because a line segment
has two endpoints. This figure has one endpoint,
point G. It is a ray, not a line segment.

IIN82   Response to Intervention • Tier 3

© Houghton Mifflin Harcourt

Do the Math

Some students may have difficulty with Problems
3-6 on student page **IIN82** because they are
more familiar with lines presented horizontally
or vertically. Guide them to see that lines, line
segments, and rays can be drawn in different
orientations.

Talk Math

- **How many endpoints does the figure in
  Problem 4 have?** one

- **In how many directions does the figure in
  Problem 6 continue?** two

Check

Ask: **How many endpoints should there be on a
line segment?** two **Does it extend beyond the
endpoints?** no

© Houghton Mifflin Harcourt

Alternative Teaching Strategy

Draw Points, Lines, Rays, Line Segments, and Planes

Objective To identify and draw points, lines, rays,
line segments, and planes

Materials ruler or straightedge

- Place students into small groups. Write the
  terms *point, line, ray, line segment,* and *plane*
  at the top of the board. Leave enough room to
  draw examples beneath each term.

- Ask: **Which of these describes an exact location
  in space?** a point Draw a point beneath the
  word point.

- Next to the point, draw a line. Ask: **How do you
  show that a line does not end?** draw an arrow
  at each end

- Say: **A ray is part of a line.** Draw a ray. Ask:
  What do you notice about the ends of the ray?
  It has an endpoint at one end and an arrow at
  the other end. Explain that this means that a ray
  continues in only one direction. Ask: **How many
  endpoints does a ray have?** one

- Say: **A line segment is also part of a line.** Draw
  a line segment. Ask: **How many endpoints does
  a line segment have?** two Explain that a line
  segment includes the endpoints and all points
  between them.

- Finally draw a parallelogram to represent a
  plane. Explain that a plane is a flat surface that
  continues in all directions.

- Tell students that geometric figures can be
  modeled by real-world objects or situations.
  Say: **When I name an object, draw what you
  think it is: *a point*, *a ray*, *a line segment*, *a line*,
  or *a plane*.**

- Call out objects, such as these: pencil line
  segment, tip of a pencil point, light that shines
  from a flashlight ray, surface of a lake plane,
  edge of the board line segment, yellow stripes
  that run down the middle of a road line,
  intersection of two streets on a map point. Give
  groups time to discuss and draw.

- For each, ask one group to explain what they
  chose to draw, and why. For lines, rays, and line
  segments, ask the group to identify the number
  of endpoints.

Response to Intervention • Tier 3   IIN82

Angles
Skill ❷

Objective
To identify right angles and angles that measure less than or greater than right angles

Materials
sheets of paper or index cards

Vocabulary
angle A figure formed by two line segments or rays that share the same endpoint

line segment A part of a line that includes two endpoints and all points between them

point An exact location in space

ray A part of a line that has one endpoint and continues without end in one direction

right angle An angle that forms a square corner and has a measures of 90°

vertex The endpoint in an angle where two rays or line segments meet

Pre-Assess
Ask students to draw a right angle on a sheet of notebook paper. Then instruct students to draw two examples of angles greater than a right angle, and two examples of angles less than a right angle.

Common Misconception
- Students may have difficulty examining angles that do not have a vertical or a horizontal ray.

- To correct this, remind students that they can turn the paper so that the angle is situated such that one ray is horizontal, or that one ray is vertical.

Discuss right angles with the class. Point out that there are many real-life objects in which right angles can be seen. These include corners

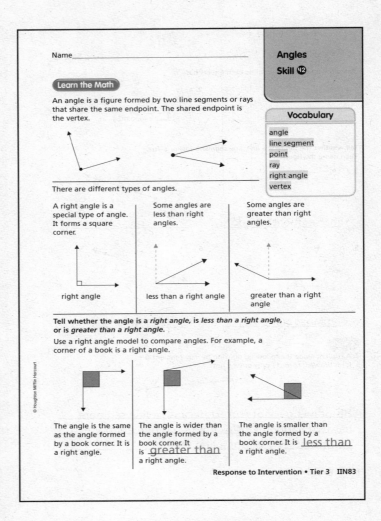

of notebook paper, doorways, and any square or rectangular object. Let students know that they can mentally compare an angle to these objects.

Go through the process of using a square corner to classify the angles on student page **IIN83**. Instruct students to line up the vertex with the corner, and one ray of the angle with one edge of a book or paper. If the other ray aligns with the second edge of the book, the angle is a right angle. If the other ray is covered by the book or paper, it is less than a right angle. If the other ray is outside the second edge of the book or paper, it is greater than a right angle.

Talk Math

- **Which of the angles on the page form corners?**
  the right angles

- **How do you know if an angle is greater than a right angle?** When I line up the vertex of the angle with the corner of a book, and one ray with an edge of the book, the second ray is outside the second edge of the book.

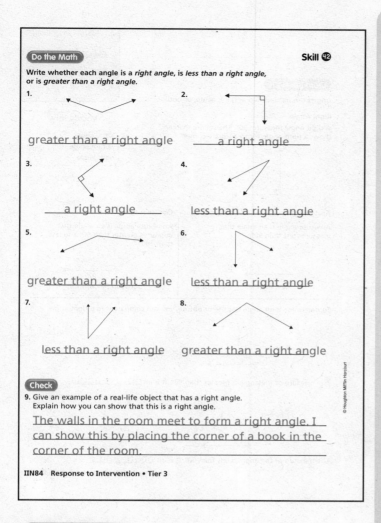

Do the Math Skill ㊷

Write whether each angle is a *right angle*, is *less than a right angle*, or is *greater than a right angle*.

1. greater than a right angle

2. a right angle

3. a right angle

4. less than a right angle

5. greater than a right angle

6. less than a right angle

7. less than a right angle

8. greater than a right angle

Check

9. Give an example of a real-life object that has a right angle. Explain how you can show that this is a right angle.

The walls in the room meet to form a right angle. I can show this by placing the corner of a book in the corner of the room.

IIN84 Response to Intervention • Tier 3

© Houghton Mifflin Harcourt

Do the Math

Have students look at student page **IIN84**. Tell students that they can turn their papers to more easily examine the angles. Instruct them to use a real-life right angle, like an index card corner, to classify the angles.

Talk Math

- **Does the angle in Problem 2 form a square corner?** yes

- **Would the angle in Problem 4 line up with the edges of a sheet of notebook paper?** no

Check

Encourage students to look around the room for objects that form square corners. Point out a few examples that might not be obvious. Examples could be the corner of the chalk-board or the door frame.

© Houghton Mifflin Harcourt

Alternative Teaching Strategy

Clock Hand Angles

Objective To identify right angles and angles that are greater than or less than right angles using a clock

Materials analog clock

- Explain to students that you are going to talk about different angles. Discuss how the hands of the clock form angles, with the vertex in the clock center.

- Ask: **What is a right angle?** an angle that forms a square corner If students have difficulty with the concept of a right angle, pick out examples in the classroom to show them. Adjacent sides of desks form right angles, for example.

- Adjust the clock to show 3:00. Ask: **Is the angle a right angle, less than a right angle, or greater than a right angle?** a right angle

- Adjust the clock to show other times and have students identify each angle as a right angle, less than a right angle, or greater than a right angle.

- At different times during the day, point to the clock and ask students if the angle formed by the hands is greater than a right angle, or less than a right angle.

- Have students explain how they know whether the angle is greater than or less than a right angle by relating the angle formed to the letter L or the corner of their desk.

Classify Angles
Skill 43

Objective
To identify right, acute, and obtuse angles

Vocabulary
acute angle An angle that measures less than a right angle (greater than 0° and less than 90°)

obtuse angle An angle that measures greater than a right angle (greater than 90° and less than 180°)

right angle An angle that forms a square corner and has a measure of 90°

Pre-Assess

Draw a right angle, an acute angle, and an obtuse angle on the board. Ask students to name each angle. Next ask students to name the type of angle that measures less than a right angle (acute) and draw an example. Also instruct students to name the type of angle that measures between 90° and 180° (obtuse) and draw an example.

Common Misconception

• Students may believe that the length of an angle's rays affects the angle's measure.

• To correct this, draw an acute angle with short rays, and ask students if the angle is acute, right, or obtuse. Then extend the rays of the angle, and ask if the angle is still acute. Repeat this activity with right angles and obtuse angles.

Learn the Math

Remind students that right angles measure exactly 90° and form square corners. Go through the examples of acute and obtuse angles on student page **IIN85**. Guide students to see that they can identify an acute angle in one of two ways: the opening is smaller than a right angle or its measure is between 0° and 90°. They can also identify an obtuse angle in two ways: the opening is wider

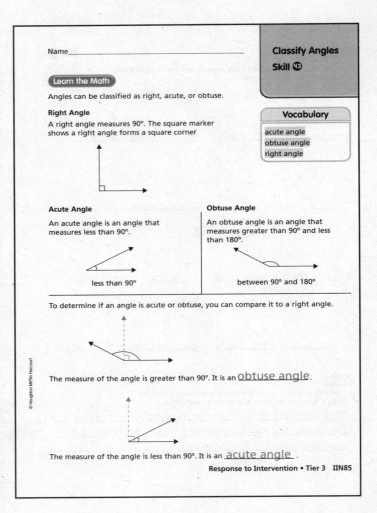

than a right angle, or its measure is between 90° and 180°.

Inform students that visual comparison to a right angle is a good way to classify an angle. Encourage them to look at a corner of a book or sheet of paper when comparing an angle to a right angle.

Talk Math

• **Is 90° the only possible measure of a right angle?** yes

• **Is an angle with a measure of 135° greater than or less than a right angle?** greater than

• **Is an angle with a measure of 45° acute, right, or obtuse?** acute

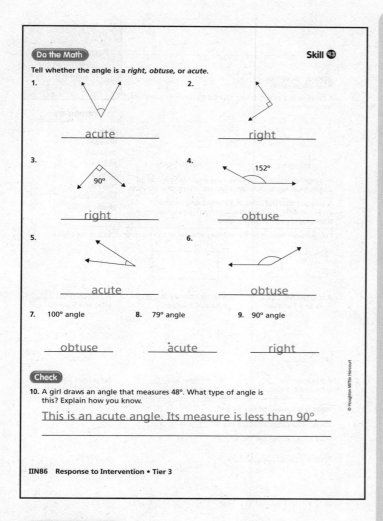

Do the Math

Skill 13

Tell whether the angle is a *right*, *obtuse*, or *acute*.

1.

acute

2.

right

3.

90°

right

4.

152°

obtuse

5.

acute

6.

obtuse

7. 100° angle

obtuse

8. 79° angle

acute

9. 90° angle

right

Check

10. A girl draws an angle that measures 48°. What type of angle is this? Explain how you know.

This is an acute angle. Its measure is less than 90°.

IIN86 Response to Intervention • Tier 3

Do the Math

Have students look at student page **IIN86**. Tell them to compare the angles to the right angle formed by a corner of a sheet of notebook paper. Have students compare the angles in Problems 1–6 to a right angle. For Problems 7–9 make sure students know they only need to compare the given angle measure to 90°.

Talk Math

• **Is the angle in Problem 1 greater or less than a right angle?** less than a right angle

• **What is the measure of the angle in Problem 2?** 90°

Check

Ask: **Is 48° equal to, less than, or greater than 90°?** less than 90°

Alternative Teaching Strategy
Angles in Letters

Objective To identify right, acute, and obtuse angles formed by English letters

• Tell students that they will analyze angles formed by letters. Instruct them to work with capital letters only.

• Write an L on the board, and ask students to write an L on a sheet of paper. Ask: **How many angles can you see in this letter?** 1 **What type of angle is it?** a right angle Write: "A right angle is 90°." on the board.

• Next, write an N on the board, and direct students to write an N on their sheet of paper. Ask: **How many angles can you see in the letter N?** 2 **What type of angles are they?** acute **Is the measure of an acute angle the same as, less than, or greater than the measure of a right angle?** less than Write: "An acute angle measures between 0° and 90°." on the board.

• Next write a X on the board, and tell students to write an X on their sheet of paper. Ask: **How many angles can you see in the letter X?** 4 Draw an arc through each of the two obtuse angles. Ask: **What type of angles are these?** obtuse **Is the measure of an obtuse angle the same as, less than, or greater than the measure of a right angle?** greater than Write: "An obtuse angle measures between 90° and 180°." on the board.

• Ask students to write 3 more letters, made of straight lines. Tell them to count and classify angles for each letter, and share the results with the class.

Response to Intervention • Tier 3   IIN86

Polygons
Skill 44

Objective
To identify, classify, and describe polygons

Vocabulary

angle A figure formed by two line segments or rays that share the same endpoint

decagon A polygon with ten sides and ten angles

hexagon A polygon with six sides and six angles

octagon A polygon with eight sides and eight angles

pentagon A polygon with five sides and five angles

polygon A closed plane figure formed by three or more line segments

quadrilateral A polygon with four sides and four angles

regular polygon A polygon with sides of equal length

triangle A polygon with three sides and three angles

Pre-Assess
Draw a triangle, quadrilateral, pentagon, hexagon, octagon, and decagon on the board, or show students models of the figures. For each figure, ask students to write the number of sides and angles. Tell students to name the polygons by the number of sides or angles.

Common Misconception

• Some students may have difficulty identifying polygons that are not regular.

• To correct this, remind students that the number of sides or the number of angles is used to classify a polygon, but only regular polygons have all sides of equal length and all angles of equal measure. Show an equilateral triangle and a scalene triangle. Students should recognize that both are triangles, but only the equilateral triangle is regular.

Name_____

Polygons
Skill 44

Learn the Math

A polygon is a closed figure formed by three or more line segments.

polygons   not polygons

In a regular polygon, all sides have equal length and all angles have equal measure. A square is a regular polygon.

A polygon that has sides of different lengths and angles of different measures is not a regular polygon. A trapezoid is not a regular polygon.

Vocabulary

angle
decagon
hexagon
pentagon
octagon
polygon
regular polygon
quadrilateral
triangle

Polygons are named by the number of sides or the number of angles they have.

A triangle has __3__ sides and 3 angles.

A quadrilateral has __4__ sides and 4 angles.

A pentagon has __5__ sides and 5 angles.

A hexagon has __6__ sides and 6 angles.

An octagon has __8__ sides and 8 angles.

A decagon has __10__ sides and 10 angles.

What is the name of this figure?

Think: How many sides are there? __5__

How many angles are there? __5__

So, it is a __pentagon__.

Response to Intervention • Tier 3 IIN87

Learn the Math

Discuss the definition of a polygon. Guide students through the first problem on student page **IIN87**. Tell students that in a closed figure all line segments must connect. Also tell students that polygons have sides which are line segments and therefore must be straight.

Ask students to count the number of sides in every figure. Help students see that the number of sides is equal to the number of angles in any given polygon.

Some of the figures shown on the page are regular polygons and some are not regular polygons. Explain that the length of sides and the measure of the angles does not affect the name of the polygon.

Talk Math

• **If a polygon has 5 angles, how many sides does it have?** 5

• **Which has more sides, a hexagon or an octagon?** an octagon

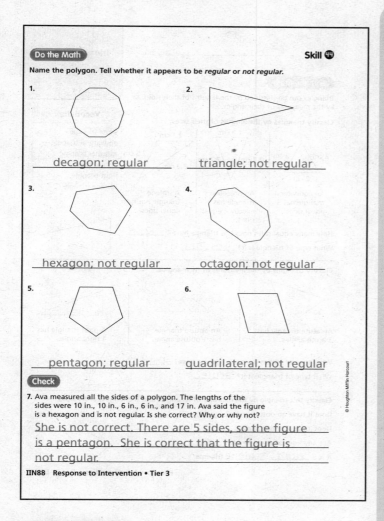

Do the Math

Skill 44

Name the polygon. Tell whether it appears to be *regular* or *not regular*.

1. decagon; regular

2. triangle; not regular

3. hexagon; not regular

4. octagon; not regular

5. pentagon; regular

6. quadrilateral; not regular

Check

7. Ava measured all the sides of a polygon. The lengths of the sides were 10 in., 10 in., 6 in., 6 in., and 17 in. Ava said the figure is a hexagon and is not regular. Is she correct? Why or why not?

She is not correct. There are 5 sides, so the figure
is a pentagon. She is correct that the figure is
not regular.

IIN88   Response to Intervention • Tier 3

Do the Math

For each of the problems on student page **IIN88**, ask students to count the number of sides and write this number on their papers. They can mark each side as they count to keep track.

Talk Math

- **How many sides and angles does the polygon in Problem 1 have?** 10

- **Why is the polygon in Problem 6 not regular?**
  The angles do not all have equal measures.

Check

Ask: **How many lengths are given?** 5 **How many sides are there in the polygon?** 5 **What is the name of the polygon that Ava measured?**
pentagon

Alternative Teaching Strategy

Naming Polygons

Objective To name various polygons based on the number of sides or the number of angles they have

Materials dot paper, demonstration-size figures including triangle, quadrilateral, pentagon, hexagon, octagon, and decagon

- Tell students polygons are named by the number of sides or the number of angles they have. Write triangle, quadrilateral, pentagon, hexagon, octagon, and decagon on the board. Tell students to copy the terms on their papers.

- Hold up examples of each figure. For each, ask the class to count the number of sides and the number of angles. Point out that number of sides = number of angles. Tell students to write the name of the polygon and the number of sides and angles it has as you display each figure (for example, pentagon: 5, decagon: 10).

- Place students in pairs. Tell every student to draw either 3, 4, 5, 6, 8 or 10 points on their sheet of dot paper. Say: **Now draw line segments to connect the points. Make sure the segments do not cross.**

- When they are finished drawing, ask pairs to exchange papers. Instruct students to write the name of the polygon, and the number of sides and the number of angles it has.

- Repeat the activity until each student has drawn all six polygons. Then collect all drawings of one type of polygon. Use them to point out that the drawings may look different if sides are of different lengths and the angles are of different measures. However, it is the number of sides and angles, not the measure that is used to classify polygons.

Response to Intervention • Tier 3   IIN88

Triangles
Skill ④⑤

Objective
To identify, describe, and classify triangles

Vocabulary

acute triangle A triangle with three acute angles

equilateral triangle A triangle with three equal, or congruent sides

isosceles triangle A triangle with exactly two equal, or congruent sides

obtuse triangle A triangle with one obtuse angle

right triangle A triangle with a right angle

scalene triangle A triangle with no equal, or congruent sides

Pre-Assess

Draw these triangles on the board: equilateral and acute (angle measures of 60°); isosceles and obtuse (angle measures such as 120°, 30°, and 30°); scalene and right. Ask students to first identify which triangle is equilateral, which is isosceles, and which is scalene, and to explain their reasoning. Next tell students to identify the obtuse, right, and acute triangles, and explain their reasoning.

Common Misconception

• Some students may only be able to classify a triangle by side lengths or by angle measures, but not both.

• To correct this, remind students that side lengths and angle measures are used in classification. Show various triangles and guide students to name them based first on angle measures, and then name them again based on side lengths.

Learn the Math

Tell students that all triangles can be classified in two ways: by the lengths of their sides or by the measures of their angles.

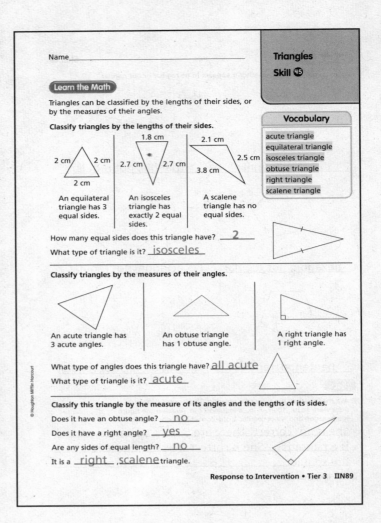

Guide students through the first set of examples on student page **IIN89**. Remind them that the short lines through two sides of the triangle mean that those sides are congruent, or of equal length.

For the second set of examples, ask students to classify each angle in each triangle as acute, obtuse, or right. Remind students of the definitions of right, acute, and obtuse angles. Show them that obtuse triangles have one obtuse angle. Discuss that it is this one obtuse angle that is used to classify the triangle as an obtuse triangle. Explain that the same is true of right triangles.

For the last section, explain that triangles can be classified by both the lengths of their sides and the measures of their angles. Refer back to the first two sections and discuss how to classify these triangles by both the lengths of their sides and the measures of their angles.

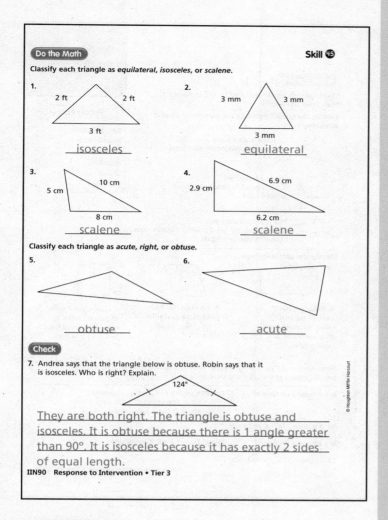

Do the Math   Skill 45

Classify each triangle as *equilateral*, *isosceles*, or *scalene*.

1.
2 ft   2 ft
3 ft
isosceles

2.
3 mm   3 mm
3 mm
equilateral

3.
5 cm   10 cm
8 cm
scalene

4.
2.9 cm   6.9 cm
6.2 cm
scalene

Classify each triangle as *acute*, *right*, or *obtuse*.

5.
obtuse

6.
acute

Check

7. Andrea says that the triangle below is obtuse. Robin says that it is isosceles. Who is right? Explain.

124°

They are both right. The triangle is obtuse and
isosceles. It is obtuse because there is 1 angle greater
than 90°. It is isosceles because it has exactly 2 sides
of equal length.

IIN90   Response to Intervention • Tier 3

Talk Math

• **Which type of triangle has no equal sides?** a scalene triangle

• **Can a triangle be both isosceles and obtuse?** yes

Do the Math

Have students look at student page IIN90. Point out that in Problems 1– 4, they are classifying triangles by the lengths of their sides, and in Problems 5 and 6 by the measures of their angles.

Talk Math

• **How many equal sides does the triangle in Problem 2 have?** three

• **Is there an obtuse angle or a right angle in the triangle in Problem 6?** no

Check

Ask: **Can a triangle be both obtuse and isosceles?** yes **Acute and isosceles?** yes **Right and isosceles?** yes

---

Alternative Teaching Strategy

Model Triangles

Objective To model isosceles, equilateral, scalene, obtuse, right, and acute triangles

Materials a large rectangle per group (can be paper or cardboard)

• Ask 9 students to volunteer to form a triangle. Explain that they will use their arms to make various triangles together. Allow all students a chance to be part of the group when making different triangles.

• Help the group to form an equilateral triangle. Say: **An equilateral triangle has three equal sides.** Ask students to stand with their arms outstretched. Explain that for this exercise, you will assume all arms are the same length. Make a triangle, directing three students to stand on each side. Say: **There are six arms on each side, so this is an equilateral triangle.**

• Next explain that an isosceles triangle has exactly two sides of equal length. Ask the group to model an isosceles triangle. 8 arms (4 students) on each of 2 sides, 2 arms (1 student) on the third side

• Finally tell students that a scalene triangle has no equal sides. Ask the group to model a scalene triangle. number of students per side: 4, 3, and 2, or 5, 3, and 1

• Next explain that triangles can also be classified by the measures of their angles. Say: **A right triangle has one right angle.** Direct the group to use the corner of the rectangle as a right angle measure, and to model a right triangle. (Two sides will stand perpendicular.)

• Now say: **An obtuse triangle has one obtuse angle.** Remind students that an obtuse angle is greater than a right angle. Using the right angle (rectangle) as reference, have the group model an obtuse triangle.

• Finally say: **An acute triangle has only acute angles.** Remind students acute angles are less than right angles, and tell the group to model an acute triangle.

Quadrilaterals
Skill ④⑥

Objective
To identify, describe, and classify quadrilaterals

Vocabulary
parallelogram A quadrilateral whose opposite sides are parallel and equal, or congruent

quadrilateral A polygon with four sides and four angles

rectangle A parallelogram with opposite sides that are equal, or congruent, and with four right angles

rhombus A parallelogram with four equal, or congruent, sides

square A parallelogram with four equal, or congruent, sides and four right angles

trapezoid A quadrilateral with exactly one pair of parallel sides

Pre-Assess
Draw a trapezoid and a parallelogram on the board. Ask students to name each figure. Then tell students to draw a rectangle, a rhombus, and a square on their papers. Ask students to explain the attributes of each figure.

Common Misconception
- Some students may classify a quadrilateral based only on pairs of parallel sides.
- To correct this, remind students that parallelograms can further be classified by the lengths of their sides and the measures of their angles.

Explain to students that quadrilaterals are classified by their number of parallel sides, side lengths, and angle measures. Discuss the concept of parallel sides. Help students identify the parallel sides in the examples at the top of student page **IIN91**.

Learn the Math

Quadrilaterals can be classified by the characteristics of their sides and angles.

Classify the quadrilaterals by the number of parallel sides they have.

Vocabulary
parallelogram
quadrilateral
rectangle
rhombus
square
trapezoid

Quadrilaterals have 4 sides. This quadrilateral has no parallel sides.

This is a trapezoid. A trapezoid has exactly 1 pair of parallel sides.

This is a parallelogram. A parallelogram has 2 pairs of parallel sides. Opposite sides are equal.

Classify the parallelograms.

A rectangle has 2 pairs of parallel sides, opposite sides that are equal, and __4__ right angles.

A rhombus has 2 pairs of parallel sides. It has __4__ equal sides.

A square has 2 pairs of parallel sides. It has __4__ equal sides and 4 right angles.

These figures are parallelograms because they have 2 pairs of parallel sides and the opposite sides are equal.

Is a square a rectangle?   Think: A square has 2 pairs of parallel sides. The opposite sides are equal. It has 4 right angles

So, a square __is__ a rectangle.

Is a square a rhombus?   Think: A square has 4 equal sides.

So, a square __is__ a rhombus.

Response to Intervention • Tier 3   IIN91

Go through the figures in the second part of the page. Remind students that these figures are all parallelograms, since they all have two pairs of parallel sides. Guide students to see that opposite sides are equal for each figure. Ask: **Which of the figures have 4 right angles?** rectangle and square **Which of the figures have 4 equal sides?** rhombus and square Help students see that a square is also a rectangle and also a rhombus, since it meets all criteria for each figure. This means that a square can be given several names: square, rectangle, rhombus, parallelogram, or quadrilateral. Point out that several quadrilaterals can be given more than one name.

Talk Math

- **Is a trapezoid a parallelogram?** no
- **Are rectangles, rhombuses, and squares all parallelograms?** yes

© Houghton Mifflin Harcourt

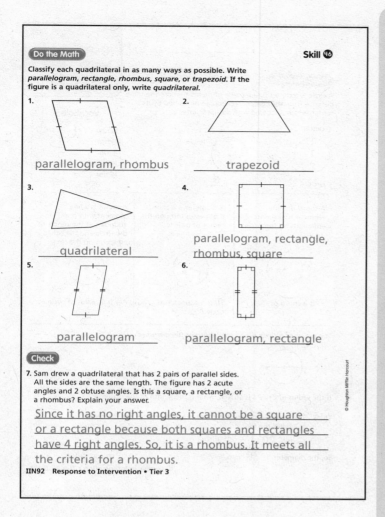

Do the Math — Skill 46

Classify each quadrilateral in as many ways as possible. Write *parallelogram, rectangle, rhombus, square,* or *trapezoid.* If the figure is a quadrilateral only, write *quadrilateral.*

1. parallelogram, rhombus

2. trapezoid

3. quadrilateral

4. parallelogram, rectangle, rhombus, square

5. parallelogram

6. parallelogram, rectangle

Check

7. Sam drew a quadrilateral that has 2 pairs of parallel sides. All the sides are the same length. The figure has 2 acute angles and 2 obtuse angles. Is this a square, a rectangle, or a rhombus? Explain your answer.

Since it has no right angles, it cannot be a square or a rectangle because both squares and rectangles have 4 right angles. So, it is a rhombus. It meets all the criteria for a rhombus.

IIN92 Response to Intervention • Tier 3

• **Which features can be used to classify quadrilaterals?** the number of pairs of parallel sides, the number of equal sides (opposite sides equal or all sides equal), and the measures of the angles

Do the Math

Guide students to classify the figures on student page **IIN92**, by first determining if a figure is a trapezoid, a parallelogram, or neither. If it is a parallelogram, direct students to classify it further by determining how many sides are equal and if it has right angles.

Talk Math

• **In Problem 1, are all sides equal?** yes **Are there any right angles?** no **Can it be a square?** no

• **Are any sides parallel in Problem 3?** no

Check

Ask: **Are there right angles?** no **Must a figure have right angles to be a square?** yes **A rectangle?** yes

---

Alternative Teaching Strategy

Drawing Quadrilaterals

Objective To model, draw, and classify quadrilaterals

Materials geoboards, rubber bands, and dot paper

• Tell students they are going to create a tree diagram to model and classify quadrilaterals. Give a geoboard to each pair of students and a sheet of dot paper to each student. Have them draw the following diagram on their papers.

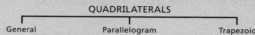

QUADRILATERALS

General   Parallelogram   Trapezoid

• Ask students to draw a 4-sided figure with no pairs of parallel sides beneath the label General. Draw an example on the board.

• Draw a trapezoid on the board and have students make a trapezoid on their geoboards. Ask: **How many pairs of parallel sides are there?** one Tell students to draw a trapezoid under the label Trapezoid on their paper.

• Draw a parallelogram and have students make a parallelogram on their geoboards. Ask: **How many pairs of parallel sides are there?** two Point out the opposite sides are equal. Instruct students to draw a parallelogram under the label Parallelogram.

• Tell students to add the labels Rectangle and Rhombus under the parallelogram.

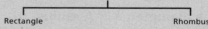

Rectangle   Rhombus

• Have students make a rectangle. Ask: **Are there any right angles?** yes **How many?** 4 **Which sides are equal?** opposite sides Ask students to draw a rectangle under the label Rectangle.

• Have students make a rhombus that does not have right angles. Ask: **Are there any right angles?** no **Which sides are equal?** all sides Ask students to draw a rhombus under the label Rhombus.

• Add the label Square to the diagram under the rectangle and the rhombus. Direct students to make and draw a square. Ask them to describe how a square is both a rectangle and a rhombus.

• Tell students to keep the tree diagrams for future reference.

Response to Intervention • Tier 3   IIN92

Circles
Skill 47

Objective
To identify the following parts of a circle: chord, diameter, and radius

Vocabulary
center The point inside a circle that is the same distance from each point on the circle

chord A line segment with endpoints on the circle

circle A closed figure made of points that are the same distance from the center

diameter A line segment that passes through the center of the circle and has endpoints on the circle

radius A line segment with one endpoint at the center of a circle and one endpoint on the circle

Pre-Assess
Draw the following circle on the board.

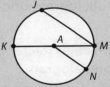

Say: **Name a diameter.** $\overline{KM}$ **A radius.** $\overline{AK}, \overline{AM},$ or $\overline{AN}$ **A chord that is not also a diameter.** $\overline{JM}$ Ask: **If the radius is 3 in., what is the diameter?** 6 in.

Common Misconception

• Students may confuse the terms *radius* and *diameter*.

• To correct this, remind students that the diameter is twice the length of the radius. It may help some students to think that the word diameter has more letters in it than the word radius, and relate diameter to be the longer line segment.

Learn the Math

Discuss the definition of circle with students. Tell them that circles are named for their center points.

IIN93   Response to Intervention • Tier 3

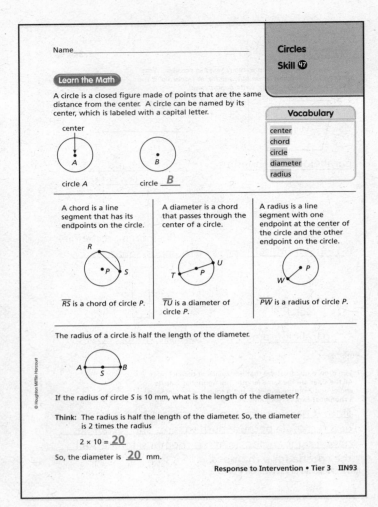

Instruct students to look at the second circle at the top of student page IIN93. Ask: **What is the name of the second circle at the top of the page?** circle B

Look at the next set of circles. Discuss the definitions of chord and diameter. Ask: **Why is a diameter also a chord?** both of its endpoints are on the circle Discuss the definition of radius.

Guide students to see that the radius of a circle is half the length of the diameter, and the center of the circle is an endpoint of the radius. Help students to find the diameter of circle S by multiplying 2 × 10. Ask: **What is 2 × 10?** 20 **What is the diameter of the circle S?** 20 mm

Talk Math

• **What are the endpoints of the diameter shown for circle S?** point A and point B

• **How can you use the length of the radius to find the length of the diameter?** multiply the radius length by 2

Do the Math

For 1–5, use the circle at the right.

1. Name the circle.

   circle N

2. Name a chord that is not a diameter.

   TU

3. Name a radius.

   NR, NV, or NS

4. Name a diameter.

   RV

5. Name another radius.

   NR, NV, or NS

Check

6. The diameter of circle R is 4 cm. Is the radius longer or shorter than 4 cm? Explain. Then find the radius.

   It is shorter than 4 cm. The radius is half the length of the diameter. The radius of circle R is 2 cm.

Do the Math

Help students see that in the circle on student page **IIN94**, there is more than one radius shown, but only one diameter is shown. Remind students where the endpoints of a chord, a diameter, and a radius lie.

Talk Math

• **Does the diameter pass through the center of the circle, or stop at the center point?** It passes through the center.

• **How many radii are shown on the circle?** 3

Check

Ask: **How are the diameter and the radius related?** The diameter is twice the length of the radius; the radius is half the length of the diameter.

Alternative Teaching Strategy

Draw Circles and Parts of Circles

Objective Identify, draw, and label parts of a circle

Materials compass and ruler

Construct the same circle and parts of the circle on the board as students construct them on their papers.

• Have students draw a point and label it with the letter A. Then ask students to set their compasses to draw a circle with a radius of 2 in. Next, use a ruler to draw a diameter and label the endpoints point B and point C. Remind students that a diameter must pass through the center of the circle.

• Ask: **What is a radius of circle A?** $\overline{AB}$ or $\overline{AC}$ Have students measure the lengths of a radius and the diameter. Ask: **What is the relationship between the radius and the diameter?** The radius is half the length of the diameter. The diameter is twice the length of the radius. **What is the length of the diameter?** 4 in.

• Have students draw a point on the circle and label it with the letter D. Tell them to draw the radius $\overline{AD}$. Ask: **Is the length of $\overline{AD}$, the same as $\overline{AB}$ and $\overline{AC}$?** yes **Why?** All the points on a circle are the same distance from the center. So, all radii in a circle have the same length.

• Instruct students to draw point F on their circle and draw line segment between point D and point F to form a chord. Students' circles should look similar to the example below at this point.

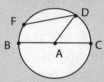

• Ask: How are $\overline{BC}$ and $\overline{DF}$ similar? They both have their endpoints on the circle. **How are they different?** $\overline{BC}$ passes through the center of the circle, $\overline{DF}$ does not.

• Instruct students to draw circle L with a diameter of 14 cm. Ask: **What will be the length of the radius?** 7 cm

• Continue to have students draw and label parts of the circle until they have practiced drawing each part of the circle: chord, diameter, and radius.

Congruent and Similar Figures
Skill 48

Objective
To identify congruent and similar figures

Materials
grid paper or dot paper, large cardboard hexagon

Vocabulary
congruent Having the same size and shape

similar Having the same shape but possibly different size

Pre-Assess

Ask students to draw a polygon on grid or dot paper. Next tell them to draw a congruent polygon, and finally instruct them to draw a polygon that is similar, but not congruent. Check students' drawings.

Common Misconception

• Students may believe that similar figures are always congruent.

• To correct this, explain that for figures to be congruent, they must have the same size and shape. Draw a large hexagon on the board by tracing around a cardboard cut-out. Ask one student to draw an exact copy of the hexagon on the board, using the cardboard. Ask the other students to draw similar hexagons on dot paper. Ask: **Are all of the hexagon drawings the same shape?** yes **Which is the same size as the original?** the one on the board Explain that only the one on the board is a congruent figure. Point out that congruent figures are similar, but not all similar figures are congruent.

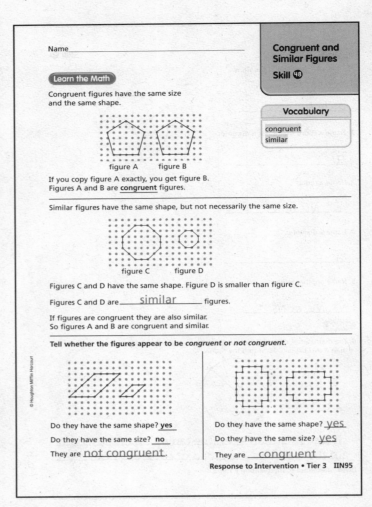

Tell students that figures which share two attributes, size and shape, are congruent. This is shown in the first problem on student page **IIN95**.

Tell students that if figures share only one attribute, shape, they are similar figures. This is shown in the second problem. Explain that if two figures do not have the same shape they are neither similar nor congruent.

Guide students to see that congruent figures are also similar, but similar figures are not always congruent.

Remind students that similar or congruent figures may be in different positions, as in the third example. If students have difficulty deciding if figures are similar or congruent because they are in different orientations, tell them they can count the lengths of the sides on the dot paper or they can trace one figure, then turn the tracing and lay it over the other figure.

Talk Math

• **If figures are not alike in shape or size, are they either similar or congruent?** no

• **What do you call figures that have the same shape but not the same size?** similar figures

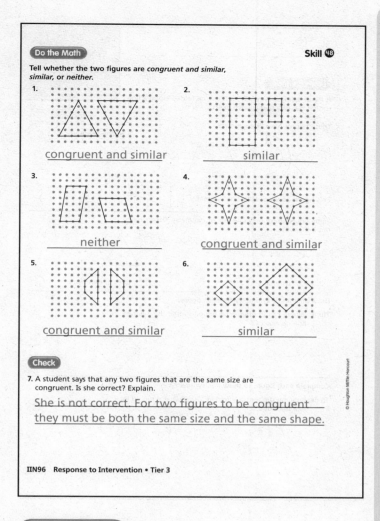

Alternative Teaching Strategy

Making Similar and Congruent Figures

Objective To create congruent and similar figures

Materials geoboards and rubber bands, or dot paper

- Give a geoboard and rubber band to each student. Use dot paper if geoboards are unavailable.

- Make a triangle on a geoboard, and hold it up for students to see. Direct students to make a congruent figure on their geoboards. Ask: **In what ways is the congruent figure like the original?** It has the same shape and is exactly the same size.

- Now make a rectangle on a geoboard, and hold it up for students to see. Instruct students to make a similar figure on their geoboards. Ask: **In what way is the similar figure like the original? How is it different?** It has the same shape, but is a different size.

- Place students in groups of 3. The students take turns playing the following roles: Student 1 makes a figure; Student 2 looks at this figure and makes a congruent figure; Student 3 makes a similar but not congruent figure.

- Tell each group to present one of their groups of figures to the class. Ask them to say which figures are congruent, which figures are similar, and to explain why in each case. Guide students to see that congruent figures share two attributes (shape and size) and similar figures sometimes share only one attribute (shape).

Do the Math

Have students look at student page **IIN96**. Remind students that if figures are close in size, but not the same shape, they are not similar or congruent.

Talk Math

- **Do any of the figure pairs on the page not have the same shape?** yes, those in problem 3

- **Can the figures in Problem 5 be congruent or similar even though they are in different positions?** Yes, it is the size and the shape of the figures that determines if they are similar or congruent, not the position.

- **In Problem 6, is one figure of the pair larger than the other?** yes

Check

Show students a circle and a square that appear to be the same size. The circle's diameter should be the same length as the square's sides. Emphasize that the circle and the square are neither congruent nor similar.

Objective
To identify and draw lines of symmetry
and symmetric figures

Materials
mirror, tracing paper, scissors

Vocabulary
line symmetry A figure has line symmetry
if it can be folded along a line so that
its two parts match exactly

Pre-Assess

Draw these figures on the board.

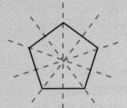 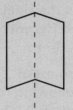 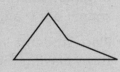

Ask students to copy them and draw at least
one line of symmetry, if the figure has line
symmetry. Ask students to explain why the third
figure does not have line symmetry. It cannot be
folded along a line so that the two parts match
exactly.

Common Misconception

• Some students may only look for vertical
  lines of symmetry and assume that if a figure
  does not have a vertical line of symmetry it is
  not symmetric.

• To correct this, remind students to look for
  vertical, horizontal, and diagonal lines of
  symmetry.

Learn the Math

Explain line symmetry. Tell students that a line
of symmetry is a line along which a figure can be
folded so that its two parts match exactly.

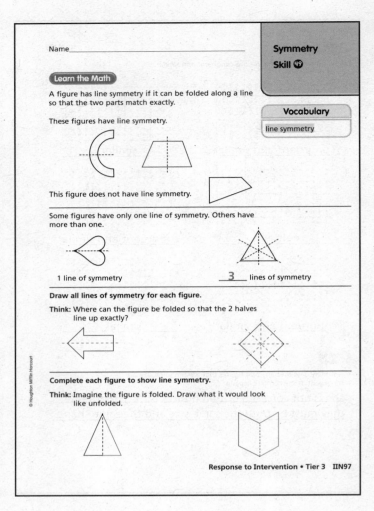

Have students place a mirror on the dashed
line in each figure to check for symmetry in
the figures shown at the top of student page
IIN97. Additionally, you can ask students to trace
the figures and the dashed lines using tracing
paper, then to fold along the line. Ask: **Do the
parts match exactly?** If yes, the line is a line of
symmetry. Help students see that any line drawn
on the quadrilateral would not be a line of
symmetry.

Students might use tracing paper or mirrors to
help them determine lines of symmetry or to
complete given figures to show symmetry.

Talk Math

• **How many lines of symmetry are there in the
  arrow figure?** one

• **Explain why a figure can have more than one
  line of symmetry.** There may be more than one
  line along which it could be folded to show
  matching halves.

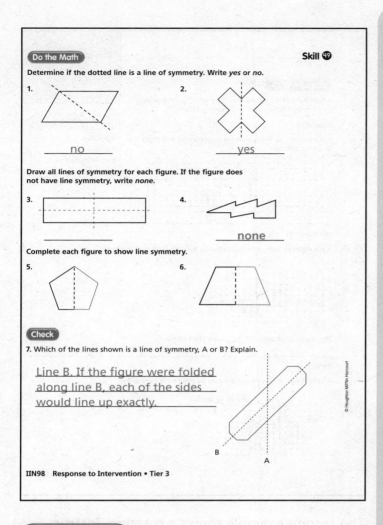

Do the Math

Skill 49

Determine if the dotted line is a line of symmetry. Write *yes* or *no*.

1.   2.

____no____   ____yes____

Draw all lines of symmetry for each figure. If the figure does not have line symmetry, write *none*.

3.   4.

_____   ____none____

Complete each figure to show line symmetry.

5.   6.

Check

7. Which of the lines shown is a line of symmetry, A or B? Explain.

Line B. If the figure were folded
along line B, each of the sides
would line up exactly.

IIN98   Response to Intervention • Tier 3

Do the Math

Remind students that a line of symmetry is a line along which a figure can be folded so that its two parts match exactly. If a figure cannot be folded so that its two parts match exactly, it does not have line symmmetry.

Talk Math

• **In Problem 1, if you folded the figure along the dotted line, would the halves match exactly?** no

• **For Problem 5, how will the other half of the figure compare to what is shown?** It will be a mirror image.

Check

Encourage students to use tracing paper or mirrors to verify that line A is not a line of symmetry.

Alternative Teaching Strategy
Drawing Symmetric Figures

Objective To draw symmetric figures using dot paper

Materials dot paper

• Draw this symmetric figure on dot paper and ask students to copy it.

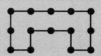

• Then ask the students to fold the paper. Draw a dashed line to show the fold.

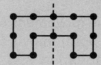

• Ask: **What do you notice about the halves of the figure as it is folded?** They match. Explain that if the halves on both sides of a line match exactly when a figure is folded, that figure has symmetry. Say: **The fold line is the line of symmetry.**

• Have students work in pairs. Explain that they are going to draw symmetric figures. First, ask each student to draw a dashed line on dot paper to represent a line of symmetry. Then direct them to draw one half of a figure, on one side of the line. Students can be creative, but provide examples as needed.

• When partners have finished drawing, tell them to switch papers. Ask students to finish their partner's figure by drawing the second half, on the other side of the line. Remind students that the halves should be mirror images, and that they can use the dots as guides to measure distances.

• Direct students to check their work by folding along the dashed line. Repeat the activity several times.

• Ask pairs to share their work with the class. Together, test to see if there are any more lines of symmetry for a given figure.

Response to Intervention • Tier 3   IIN98

Transformations
Skill ⑤⓪

Objective
To identify the movement of a figure as a translation, rotation, or a reflection

Vocabulary
reflection A movement of a figure to a new position by flipping the figure over a line

rotation A movement of a figure to a new position by turning the figure around a point

transformation The movement of a figure to a new position by a rotation, reflection, or translation

translation A movement of a figure to a new position along a straight line

Pre-Assess

Tell students they will model transformations using a sheet of notebook paper. First ask them to translate the paper to a new position. Then instruct them to rotate the paper around a point. Finally, instruct them to flip the paper over an imaginary line. Ask: **What transformation flips a figure over a line?** reflection

Common Misconception

- Students may confuse the terms translation, rotation, and reflection.

- To correct this, share several examples of each. For some students it may be helpful to point out that a translation is to slide an object along a line. Both words have the letter combination sl. A reflection is to flip an object over a line. Both words have the letter combination fl.

Learn the Math

For the first example on student page **IIN99,** ask students to trace the figure, cut it out, then use the cut-out to act out the translation.

Learn the Math

A transformation is the movement of a figure to a new position by a translation, rotation, or reflection.

Vocabulary
reflection
rotation
transformation
translation

Translation

A translation, or slide, moves a figure along a straight line to a new position.

Rotation

A rotation, or turn, moves a figure by turning it around a point.

The figure is rotated 90°, or $\frac{1}{4}$ turn, clockwise.

Reflection

A reflection, or flip, moves a figure by flipping it over a line.

Line of reflection

The second example shows a rotation. Instruct students to trace the first figure. Tell them to turn their paper clockwise to see the rotated figure. Explain that rotations are not always clockwise, they may also be counterclockwise.

For the third exmple, guide students to identify the line that the figure is flipped over and tell students this line is called the line of reflection. Note that the line may be horizontal, vertical, or diagonal. Point out that the reflection is a mirror image of the original figure. Ask students to trace the figure on the left, cut it out, and use the figure to act out the refection.

Talk Math

- **Does the size or shape of a figure change by a translation?** no

- **In the third example, what does the dashed line represent?** It is the line the figure is flipped over.

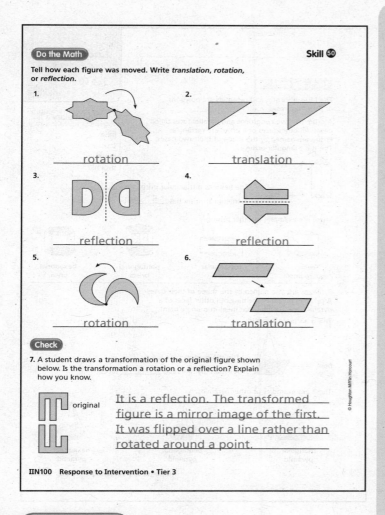

Do the Math

For each problem on student page **IIN100**, have students check to see if the figure slid along a straight line (translation), turned around a point (rotation), or flipped over a line (reflection). For Problems 3 and 4, help students see that after a reflection the figure is a mirror image of the original.

Talk Math

- **In Problem 5, was the figure rotated clockwise or counterclockwise?** counterclockwise

- **Which problems show mirror images?** 3 and 4

Check

Ask: **How does the transformation relate to the original?** It is a mirror image. Guide students to see that turning the original cannot achieve the transformation.

Alternative Teaching Strategy

Polygon Transformation

Objective To perform transformations of polygons.

Materials paper, cardboard, scissors, colored pencils

- Tell students they will model transformations of polygons. Review the meaning of *transformation*. Then ask students to draw a 4- to 6-sided polygon on cardboard (with at least 2 sides of different lengths) and cut it out.

- Direct students to place the cardboard polygon on a piece of paper, and trace around it with a black pencil. After tracing, tell them to slide the polygon to the corner of the paper, without lifting or turning it. Ask them to trace it with a different color pencil. Ask: **What is this transformation called?** translation Write *translation* and its definition on the board, and guide students to see that a transformation does not alter polygon shape or size; it only alters position.

- Ask students to place the cardboard polygon on a new piece of paper, and trace around it with a black pencil. After tracing, tell them to draw a point on a vertex. Without lifting the cardboard from the paper, guide them to turn the polygon around this point, between $\frac{1}{4}$ and $\frac{1}{2}$ turn, then to trace it again with a new color pencil. Ask: **What is this transformation called?** rotation Write and define *rotation* on the board.

- Instruct students to place the cardboard polygon on a new piece of paper, and trace it once more. After tracing, tell them to draw a dashed line segment about one half of an inch from a side or a vertex of the polygon. Direct students to flip the polygon over the dashed line segment, and to trace it again with a different color pencil. Ask: **What is this transformation called?** reflection Write and define *reflection*.

- To extend the activity, put students in pairs or groups. Direct a student to hold up one of his or her sheets of paper, and another student to name the transformation. Ask groups to share their drawings with the class.

Faces of Solid Figures
Skill 51

Objective
To identify prisms and pyramids by the shape of their bases

Materials
solid figures

Vocabulary
base A solid figure's face by which the figure is measured or named

face A polygon that is a flat surface of a solid figure

prism A solid figure with two parallel, congruent polygon-shaped bases, and other faces that are all rectangles

pyramid A solid figure with a polygon base and triangular sides that meet a single point

Pre-Assess
Show the students a rectangular prism, a cube, a triangular prism, a hexagonal prism, a square pyramid, and a triangular pyramid. Have them identify each solid figure and ask them to name the polygons, or plane figures, that make up the faces for each.

Common Misconception
• Students may mix up the words *base* and *face*.

• To correct this, remind students that all the flat surfaces of a solid figure are faces. The base, or bases, are the faces by which the figure is named.

Learn the Math
Hold up a model of a triangular prism. Tell students that all the flat surfaces of the solid figure are called faces. Point out that the triangular faces are the bases, and that these faces are parallel and congruent. Refer to student page **IIN101**. Ask students to identify the bases

IIN101 Response to Intervention • Tier 3

Name_____

Faces of Solid Figures
Skill 51

Learn the Math

The faces of prisms and pyramids are polygons, or plane figures.

A prism has two congruent and parallel faces called bases. All other faces of a prism are rectangles. Prisms are named by the shape of their two bases. This is a triangular prism.

Vocabulary
base
face
prism
pyramid

The bases of a triangular prism are <u>triangles</u>.
A triangular prism has __5__ faces.

These are examples of other prisms.

cube, square prism   rectangular prism   pentagonal prism   hexagonal prism

Pyramids are also named by the shape of their bases. A pyramid only has one base. All other faces of a pyramid are triangles that meet at a single point. This is a square pyramid.

base →

The shape of its base is a <u>square</u>.
A square pyramid has __5__ faces.

These are examples of other pyramids.

triangular pyramid   pentagonal pyramid   hexagonal pyramid

Response to Intervention • Tier 3   IIN101

---

and number of faces for each prism.

Hold up a model of a square pyramid. To help students distinguish pyramids from prisms, point out that pyramids have only one base. Assist students in completing the second problem by asking them to identify the base and count the number of faces of the square pyramid. Ask students to identify the base and the number of faces for each pyramid.

Talk Math

• **How many faces does a rectangular prism have?** 6

• **How many faces of a rectangular prism are bases?** 2

• **How many faces does a hexagonal pyramid have?** 7

• **How many faces of a pyramid are bases?** 1

© Houghton Mifflin Harcourt

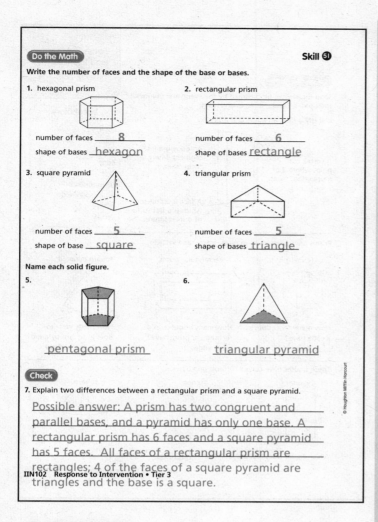

Do the Math

For Problems 1–4 on student page **IIN102**, remind students that a base is one of the faces too. Give models of the solids to students who are struggling. For Problems 5 and 6, encourage students to refer back to student page **IIN101**.

Talk Math

- **How many faces does the figure in Problem 2 have?** 6

- **How many faces does the figure in Problem 5 have?** 7 **What is the shape of the bases?** pentagon

Check

Guide students to compare the number of bases, number of faces, and shape of the faces of the two different solid figures.

© Houghton Mifflin Harcourt

Alternative Teaching Strategy
Constructing Solid Figures

Objective To make solid figures using plane shapes

Materials cardboard polygons: three pairs of congruent rectangles (the width of the second pair should equal the width of the first pair, the length of the third pair should equal the length of the first pair, the width of the third pair should equal the length of the second pair), seven congruent squares, four congruent triangles (with side length equal to the side length of the squares); tape; scissors

- Pass out cardboard polygons and tape, to each student or pair of students. Tell them you would like them to make a rectangular prism, a square pyramid, and a cube from the shapes.

- Ask: **What shapes make up the faces of a rectangular prism?** rectangles

- Ask: **How many bases does a rectangular prism have?** 2 **How are they related to each other?** They are congruent and parallel. Have students choose two rectangles for the bases.

- Ask: **How are the shapes of the front and back faces related?** The front and back faces are congruent rectangles. Have students choose two rectangles for the front and back. Repeat with the left and right faces.

- Allow students or groups to tape the sides together to construct the solid figure.

- Repeat the process to make square pyramids and cubes.

- Ask: **What polygons would you need to make a triangular prism?** 2 congruent triangles, 3 rectangles **A pentagonal prism?** 2 congruent pentagons, 5 rectangles **A hexagonal prism?** 2 congruent hexagons, 6 rectangles

- Ask: **What polygons would you need to make a triangular pyramid?** 4 triangles **A pentagonal pyramid?** 1 pentagon, 5 triangles **A hexagonal pyramid?** 1 hexagon, 6 triangles

- Have students cut out the cardboard and make a different prism or pyramid. Encourage students to make the sides of each base the same length so that all other faces will be congruent.

Faces, Edges and Vertices
Skill 52

Objective
To count the number of faces, edges, and vertices on prisms and pyramids; to identify cones, cylinders, and spheres

Materials
solid figures

Vocabulary
cone A solid figure that has a flat circular base

cube A solid figure with six congruent square faces

cylinder A solid figure that has two parallel bases that are congruent circles

edge The line segment where two faces of a solid figure meet

face A polygon that is a flat surface of a solid figure

rectangular prism A solid figure in which all six faces are rectangles

square pyramid A solid figure with a square base and four triangular faces that have a common vertex

sphere A round object whose curved surface is the same distance from the center to all of its points

vertex The point where three or more edges meet in a solid figure; the top point of a cone

Pre-Assess
Show students a cylinder, cone, and sphere. Ask them to name each object. Then show a cube, rectangular prism, and square pyramid. Ask them to name and say the number of faces, edges and vertices for each.

Common Misconception
• Some students may confuse edge and vertex.

• To correct this, remind them that an edge is where faces meet, and a vertex is where edges meet.

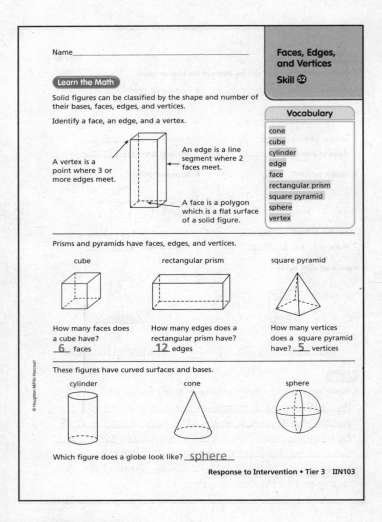

Learn the Math

Have students identify a vertex, an edge, and a face on the rectangular prism at the top of student page **IIN103**. Help students count the number of edges that meet at the vertex. Tell them the plural of vertex is vertices.

Tell students to name each figure in the second row. For the rectangular prism, remind students to count each edge only once. Ask students to mark all the vertices of the pyramid.

The bottom row introduces figures with curved surfaces. You may ask students to identify real-world objects that have these shapes.

Talk Math

• **How many edges meet at the top vertex of the square pyramid?** 4

• **Which has more vertices, a square pyramid or a rectangular prism?** rectangular prism

Skill 52 — Do the Math

Do the Math

Name a solid figure for each description.

1. 8 vertices, 12 edges, 6 faces

   cube or
   rectangular prism

2. 4 triangular faces, 1 square face

   square pyramid

3. 2 circular bases

   cylinder

4. 6 square faces

   cube

Find the number of edges and vertices for each figure.

5.

   _8_ edges   _5_ vertices

6.

   _12_ edges   _8_ vertices

Find the number of faces for each solid figure.

7.

   _6_ faces

8.

   _5_ faces

Check

9. Anderson said that this figure is a cone. Is he correct? Why or why not?

   He is not correct. A cone has curved
   surfaces and a circular base. This
   figure has a square base and no
   curved surfaces.

Do the Math

For Problems 1–4 on student page **IIN104**, direct students to refer to the figures on the previous page. For in Problems 5–8, suggest that students try to name each figure before they count the faces, edges, or vertices.

Talk Math

- **Does a square pyramid have more edges or vertices?** edges

- **How many edges does a cube have?** 12

Check

Ask: **What does the base of a cone look like?** a circle **Does the figure in Problem 9 have curved surfaces?** no

Alternative Teaching Strategy

Count Faces, Edges, and Vertices

Objective To identify and count faces, edges, and vertices of solid figures

Materials paper cubes, rectangular prisms, and square pyramids of various sizes; markers

- Put students in small groups and tell them they will examine solid figures. Give each group a cube. Ask students to point to the square surfaces of the cube. Ask: **What is the name of these flat surfaces?** faces

- Explain that an edge is where two faces meet. Count the cube's edges together with the class. Ask: **How many edges does a cube have?** 12

- Say that a corner of the cube is called a vertex. Point to a vertex and ask: **How many edges meet at this point?** 3 Explain that three or more edges meet at a vertex in a solid figure.

- Now give a different solid to each group. Tell groups to number each face, starting with 1. Ask them to record the number of faces, and the shape of each face.

- Direct each student to touch an edge of the solid figure. Ask them to count and record the number of edges. Then have each student touch a vertex. Instruct students to count and record the number of vertices.

- Next, ask each group to give you one of their papers that has the number of faces, edges, and vertices of their solid figure and to place their solid figure at the front of the room.

- Hand the papers out to groups in random order. Instruct them to use the descriptions to choose the correct solid figure.

- Repeat several times. Ask groups to show their figure's faces, edges, and vertices to the class.

Objective

To choose appropriate customary units or metric units for measuring length and distance

Materials

inch ruler, centimeter ruler, yardstick, meterstick

Vocabulary

centimeter A metric unit used to measure length or distance

foot A customary unit for measuring length or distance; 1 foot = 12 inches

inch A customary unit used to measure length or distance

kilometer A metric unit for measuring length or distance; 100 meters = 1 kilometer

meter A metric unit for measuring length or distance; 100 centimeters = 1 meter

mile A customary unit for measuring length or distance; 5,280 feet = 1 mile

yard A customary unit for measuring length or distance; 3 feet = 1 yard

Pre-Assess

Instruct students to give two situations in which they describe length in real life. Common examples are the distance from home to school, or length of a pair of pants. Show them rulers, yardsticks and metersticks. Ask them which units they would use for the two lengths. Ask: **Would you use the same units for both situations? Why or why not?** Answers will vary.

Common Misconception

• Students may have a hard time choosing between units of feet and yards.

• To correct this, remind students that a yard is three times longer than a foot. Have them think about which form of measurement would have the fewest units, without having a unit of less than one.

Name_____

Learn the Math

Length and distance can be measured in customary units or metric units.

Customary Units

Vocabulary

centimeter
foot
inch
kilometer
meter
mile
yard

inch (in.)	foot (ft)	yard (yd)	mile (mi)
The length of a paperclip is about 1 inch.	The length of a piece of notebook paper is about 1 foot.	A yard is about the length of a baseball bat.	A mile is about the distance you can walk in 20 minutes.

Choose the appropriate customary unit to measure each object. Write *inches*, *feet*, *yards*, or *miles*.

• the width of a mug   **inches**
• a child's height   **feet**
• the distance between two airports   **miles**
• the length of a hallway   **feet or yards**

Metric Units

centimeter (cm)	meter (m)	kilometer (km)
The length of a fingernail is about 1 cm.	A meter is about the width of a door.	A kilometer is about the distance you can walk in 10 minutes.

Choose the appropriate metric unit to measure each object. Write *meters*, *kilometers*, or *centimeters*.

• the height of a tree   **meters**
• the length of a flower petal   **centimeters**
• the distance from New York to Los Angeles **kilometers**

Response to Intervention • Tier 3   IIN105

Learn the Math

Guide students through the problems on student page **IIN105** by having them identify which units are used for small lengths, which are used for long lengths, and which are used for very long lengths or distances. For each measurement, ask: **Is it a short, long, or very long length?** Answers will vary.

Talk Math

• **Can the width of a mug be more easily compared to the length of some quarters or to the length of a table?** the length of some quarters

• **How long would it take to walk a distance equal to the height of a tree?** Possible answer: it would take less than a minute.

© Houghton Mifflin Harcourt

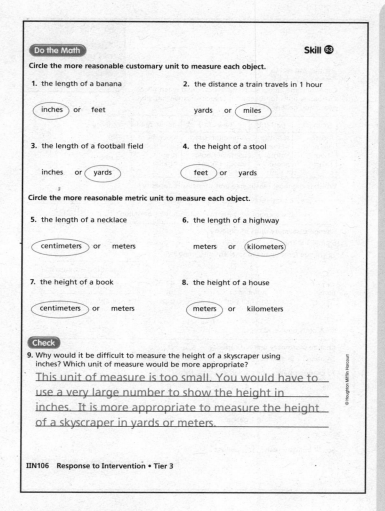

Do the Math

For each problem on student page **IIN106**, ask students to first identify whether the length or distance is very short or long. Help them to rank the units from least to greatest.

Talk Math

- **For Problem 2, is this a short distance or a long distance?** This is a long distance.

- **Which measurement unit is larger, meters or kilometers?** kilometers

Check

Ask: **What length would be closest to the length of a skyscraper: the length of a baseball bat or the length of a football field?** the length of a football field Help students estimate the height of a skyscraper.

Alternative Teaching Strategy
Measure Length

Objective To choose appropriate customary or metric units for measuring length of objects in the classroom

Materials inch ruler, centimeter ruler, yardstick, meterstick

- Hand out the rulers, yardstick and meterstick to students. Start the activity using customary units. Then repeat it using metric units.

- Tell students to find the inch mark on the ruler and yardstick. Ask: **How many inches are there in 1 foot?** 12 **How many feet are there in 1 yard?** 3 Tell them that there are 5,280 feet in 1 mile, so a mile is a unit that is too large for measuring lengths of classroom objects.

- Write this chart for students to copy.

Object	Unit	Est. Length	Actual Length

- Have students select five or more classroom objects, and write their names in the first column.

- Then have students choose units to measure their objects, filling in the second column. Remind them to choose a unit in which the measurement will be close to or greater than 1. As an example, say: **You would not use feet to measure a piece of chalk, since the length of a piece of chalk is much less than 1 foot.**

- Tell students to estimate object lengths using their chosen units and record the estimates in the chart. Then have students measure and record the actual measurements.

- Ask: **Were any of your units not appropriate for the measurement?** Possible answer: Yards were not appropriate for measuring notebook paper, since its length is less than 1 yard. Have students choose new units and repeat measurements for any of these cases.

Response to Intervention • Tier 3   IIN106

Customary Units of Capacity
Skill 54

Objective
To relate cups, quarts, pints and gallons

Materials
cup, pint, quart and gallon containers

Vocabulary
capacity The amount a container can hold when filled

cup (c) A customary unit for measuring capacity; 8 ounces = 1 cup

gallon (gal) A customary unit for measuring capacity; 1 gallon = 4 quarts

pint (pt) A customary unit for measuring capacity; 1 pint = 2 cups

quart (qt) A customary unit for measuring capacity; 1 quart = 2 pints

Pre-Assess
Ask students to fill in the conversion chart below.

1 pint (pt)	_2_ cups (c)
1 quart (qt)	_2_ pints
1 gallon (gal)	_4_ quarts

Then ask students to find:
1. How many pints are in 2 quarts? 4
2. How many cups are in 4 pints? 8
3. How many gallons are in 8 quarts? 2
4. How many pints are in 16 cups? 8

Encourage students to explain their work.

Common Misconception

• Some students may not remember when to use multiplication and when to use division when converting units.

• To correct this, tell students to first determine whether they are changing from larger to smaller units or from smaller to larger units. Remind students to multiply when converting from larger to smaller units and to divide when converting from smaller to larger units.

Learn the Math

Explain to students that the cup, pint, quart,

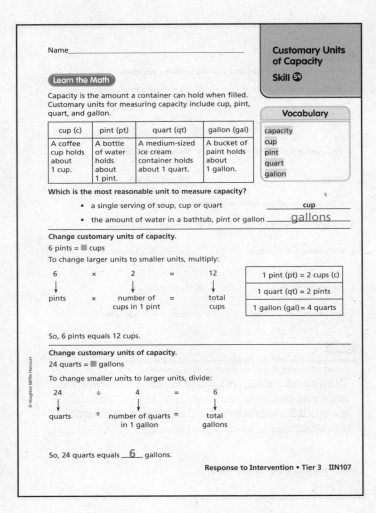

and gallon are customary units for measuring liquid. Read the chart at the top of student page **IIN107**. Show students 1-cup, 1-pint, 1-quart, and 1-gallon containers, arranged from smallest capacity to largest capacity.

Have students look at the second problem and the conversion table in the middle of the page. Tell student they should always multiply when changing from a larger unit of capacity (number given) to a smaller unit (number to be determined). You might practice other conversions with students. For example, ask: **How many quarts are in 2 gallons?** 8

Use the conversion table for the problem at the bottom of the page. Guide students to see that division is used to change from smaller units of capacity to larger units.

Talk Math

• **For the second problem, is the number of pints or the number of cups known?** pints **Which is larger, pints or cups?** pints

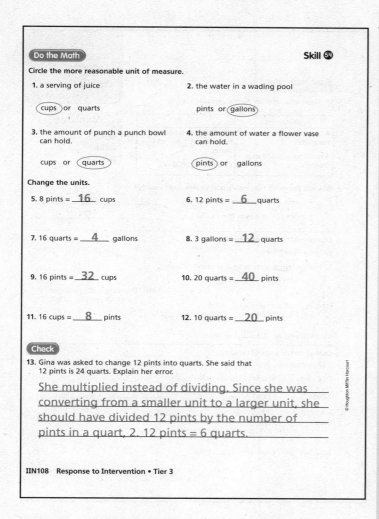

Do the Math Skill 54

Circle the more reasonable unit of measure.

1. a serving of juice

(cups) or quarts

2. the water in a wading pool

pints or (gallons)

3. the amount of punch a punch bowl can hold.

cups or (quarts)

4. the amount of water a flower vase can hold.

(pints) or gallons

Change the units.

5. 8 pints = __16__ cups

6. 12 pints = __6__ quarts

7. 16 quarts = __4__ gallons

8. 3 gallons = __12__ quarts

9. 16 pints = __32__ cups

10. 20 quarts = __40__ pints

11. 16 cups = __8__ pints

12. 10 quarts = __20__ pints

Check

13. Gina was asked to change 12 pints into quarts. She said that 12 pints is 24 quarts. Explain her error.

She multiplied instead of dividing. Since she was converting from a smaller unit to a larger unit, she should have divided 12 pints by the number of pints in a quart, 2. 12 pints = 6 quarts.

IIN108 Response to Intervention • Tier 3

- **Which operation do you use to change from larger units to smaller units?** multiplication

- **Which operation do you use to change from smaller units to larger units?** division

Do the Math

For the problems on student page **IIN108**, ask students to refer to benchmarks for each unit of capacity. For Problems 5–12, tell them to write down the operation to use in the conversion.

Talk Math

- **In Problem 1, is a quart a single serving?** no

- **In Problem 8, which is the larger unit?** gallons **Which operation do you use for this problem?** multiplication

Check

Guide students to see that the conversion is from a smaller to a larger unit. Ask: **Which operation did she use?** multiplication **Which operation is needed to convert from a smaller to a larger unit?** division

Alternative Teaching Strategy
Compare Customary Units of Capacity

Objective To compare cups, pints, quarts, gallons

Materials water, funnel, 1-cup measures, 1 pint containers, 1 quart containers, 1 gallon containers

- Divide students into pairs. Explain that they will explore customary units of capacity. Write the chart below on the board, and ask students to copy it on a sheet of paper.

1 pint (pt)	= ___ cups (c)
1 quart (qt)	= ___ pints
1 gallon (gal)	= ___ quarts

- Instruct students to use a 1-cup measure to fill the pint container. Ask: **How many cups are in 1 pint?** 2 Direct students to fill in this number in the chart.

- Repeat this activity, using the pint container to fill the quart container, and the quart container to fill the gallon container. 1 qt = 2 pints; 1 gal = 4 quarts

- Next join pairs of students into groups of 6. Write *2 pints = ? cups* on the board, and tell groups to find the number of cups in 2 pints, using their containers. 4 Write this number in the equation on the board.

- Refer to *2 pints = 4 cups.* Ask: **Which is the larger unit?** pints Guide students to see that if they multiply the number of pints by the number of cups in 1 pint, they get the answer (4 cups). Say: **To change a larger unit to a smaller unit, multiply.**

- Next, write *6 cups = ? pints* on the board. Tell students to see how many pints six 1-cup measures will fill. 3 Write this number in the equation.

- Refer to *6 cups = 3 pints.* Ask: **Which is the smaller unit?** cups Guide students to see that if they divide the number of cups by the number of cups in 1 pint, they get the answer (3 pints). Say: **To change a smaller unit to a larger unit, divide.**

- Ask students to solve the following by multiplication or division: 4 gallons = ? quarts, 6 pints = ? quarts, 8 cups = ? pints. Tell them to check their answers using containers. 16; 3; 4

Response to Intervention • Tier 3 IIN108

Objective

To relate milliliters to liters

Materials

dropper, 1-liter container

Vocabulary

capacity The amount a container can hold when filled

milliliter A metric unit for measuring capacity; 1 liter = 1,000 milliliters

liter A metric unit for measuring capacity; 1 liter = 1,000 milliliters

Pre-Assess

Ask students to say whether they would measure the water in a wading pool in liters or milliliters. Explain. Liters. A liter is a larger unit than a milliliter, and a milliliter is only about the capacity of a dropper. Then ask students to find:

1. How many milliliters are in 1 liter? 1,000
2. How many liters are in 8000 milliliters? 8

Common Misconception

- Some students may not remember which operation to use when converting between liters and milliliters.

- To correct this, tell students to first determine whether they are converting from liters to milliliters or from milliliters to liters. Remind students to multiply by 1,000 when changing liters to milliliters and to divide by 1,000 when changing from milliliters to liters.

Learn the Math

Explain to students that milliliters and liters are metric units for measuring capacity. Go through the examples in the first problem on student page **IIN109**. Show students a dropper, which holds about 1 milliliter, and a 1-liter container. Ask students to keep these benchmarks in mind

---

Name_____

Learn the Math

Milliliters and liters are metric units of capacity.

milliliter (mL)	liter (L)
A dropper holds about 1 milliliter. A milliliter is less than a spoonful.	A plastic sports bottle holds about 1 liter of water. One liter is 1,000 mL.

Vocabulary

capacity
milliliter
liter

Which is the more reasonable unit to measure capacity?

- a dose of medication, 10 mL or 10 L   10 mL
- a sink full of water, 10 ml or 10 L   10 L

Change metric units of capacity.

5 liters = ▮ milliliters

To change larger units to smaller units, multiply:

$$5 \times 1,000 = 5,000$$

liters × number of mL in 1 liter = total milliliters

Think: There are 1,000 milliliters in 1 liter. Multiply by 1,000.

So, 5 liters equals 5,000 milliliters.

Change metric units of capacity.

2,000 milliliters = ▮ liters

To change smaller units to larger units, divide:

$$2,000 \div 1,000 = 2$$

liters ÷ number of mL in 1 liter = total milliliters

Think: There are 1,000 milliliters in 1 liter. Divide by 1,000.

So, 2,000 milliliters equals 2 liters.

Response to Intervention · Tier 3   IIN109

© Houghton Mifflin Harcourt

---

when finding a reasonable measurement for a dose of medication.

For the second problem, guide students to see that multiplication is used specifically to change liters (the larger unit) to milliliters (the smaller unit). Any liter value can be changed to milliliters by multiplying by 1,000.

For the third problem, help students to see that division is the operation used to change milliliters (the smaller unit) to liters (the larger unit). Any milliliter value can be changed to liters by dividing by 1,000.

Talk Math

- **How many milliliters are in 1 liter?** 1,000

- **Explain how you would change 6 liters into milliliters.** Multiply 6 by 1,000.

- **Which operation is used to change milliliters to liters?** division

© Houghton Mifflin Harcourt

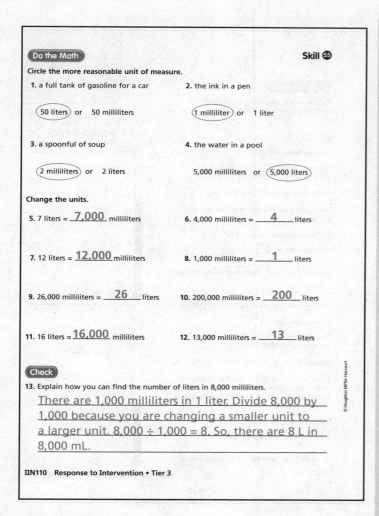

Do the Math

Skill 55

Circle the more reasonable unit of measure.

1. a full tank of gasoline for a car

(50 liters) or   50 milliliters

2. the ink in a pen

(1 milliliter) or   1 liter

3. a spoonful of soup

(2 milliliters) or   2 liters

4. the water in a pool

5,000 milliliters or (5,000 liters)

Change the units.

5. 7 liters = __7,000__ milliliters

6. 4,000 milliliters = __4__ liters

7. 12 liters = __12,000__ milliliters

8. 1,000 milliliters = __1__ liters

9. 26,000 milliliters = __26__ liters

10. 200,000 milliliters = __200__ liters

11. 16 liters = __16,000__ milliliters

12. 13,000 milliliters = __13__ liters

Check

13. Explain how you can find the number of liters in 8,000 milliliters.

There are 1,000 milliliters in 1 liter. Divide 8,000 by 1,000 because you are changing a smaller unit to a larger unit. 8,000 ÷ 1,000 = 8. So, there are 8 L in 8,000 mL.

IIN110   Response to Intervention • Tier 3

© Houghton Mifflin Harcourt

Do the Math

For Problems 1-4 on student page **IIN110**, ask students to compare the descriptions to the benchmarks for a milliliter and a liter. For Problems 5–12, ask students to tell which operation is needed.

Talk Math

• **In Problem 1, which is larger: 50 L or 50 mL?** 50 L

• **In Problem 5, which operation should you use?** multiplication

Check

Guide students to see that the conversion is from milliliters to liters. Ask: **Which operation is used to change milliliters to liters?** division

Alternative Teaching Strategy

Metric Units of Capacity

Objective To change milliliters to liters and liters to milliliters

Materials 1-centimeter cubes, 1-liter containers, 2-liter containers, labeling tape and a marker

• Have students work with a partner. Explain that they will explore metric units of capacity.

• Ask students to pick up one 1-centimeter cube. Say: **If this cube was filled with liquid, it would hold 1 milliliter of liquid.** Next tell students to pick up the 1-liter container. Say: **If this container was filled with liquid, it would hold 1 liter of liquid.** Finally instruct the students to look at the 2-liter container. Say: **If this container was filled with liquid, it would hold 2 liters of liquid.** Ask students to label each object.

• Instruct the students to arrange the objects in order from smallest capacity to largest capacity. Ask: **Which is greater: a milliliter or a liter?** a liter

• Direct students to work together to decide if these things are more than, less than, or about the same as a liter: a mug of tea less than, a filled bird bath more than, a large bottle of water about the same as. Ask them to share their answers. Ask: **Can you think of anything that may be about a milliliter?** Possible answers: eye drops, tears, raindrops, drops of glue.

• Write *1 liter (L) = 1,000 milliliters (mL)*. Ask: **Which container holds 1,000 milliliters?** the 1-L container

• Ask: **How many milliliters are in 2 liters?** Guide students to think about the number of milliliters that could fit into the 2-liter container. 2,000 Say: **To convert liters to milliliters, multiply by 1,000.**

• Tell students that to convert from milliliters to liters you use the opposite operation. Ask: **How do you convert 3,000 milliliters to liters?** Divide by 1,000. How many liters are in 3,000 milliliters? 3

• Ask students to practice converting between milliliters and liters by completing the following problems: 6,000 mL = ? L 6; 9 L = ? mL 9,000; 11 L = ? mL 11,000; 1,300 mL = ? L 13

Response to Intervention • Tier 3   IIN110

Read a Thermometer Skill 56

Objective
To read temperature on a Fahrenheit or Celsius thermometer

Materials
Fahrenheit/Celsius thermometer

Vocabulary
degree Celsius A metric unit for measuring temperature; on the Celsius scale, the freezing point of water is 0°C and the boiling point of water is 100°C

degree Fahrenheit A standard unit for measuring temperature; on the Fahrenheit scale, the freezing point of water is 32°F and the boiling point of water is 212°F

Pre-Assess
Show the class a thermometer with Fahrenheit and Celsius scales. Explain to them that the thermometer shows the temperature of the room. Ask volunteers to read the temperature in both degrees Fahrenheit and degrees Celsius. Tell students that the temperature outside is warmer/cooler. Ask: **If the thermometer were outside, would the reading be higher or lower? Why?** If you have an outside thermometer visible through the window, have students read the outside temperature.

Common Misconception
- Students might confuse Fahrenheit and Celsius if they are not familiar with these scales.

- To correct this, explain to them that a comfortable room temperature on the Fahrenheit scale is around 72°, while on the Celsius scale it is around 22°. It may also help to point out other benchmarks such as the freezing point and boiling point of water.

Learn the Math
Guide students through the examples on student page **IIN111**. Have them point to the

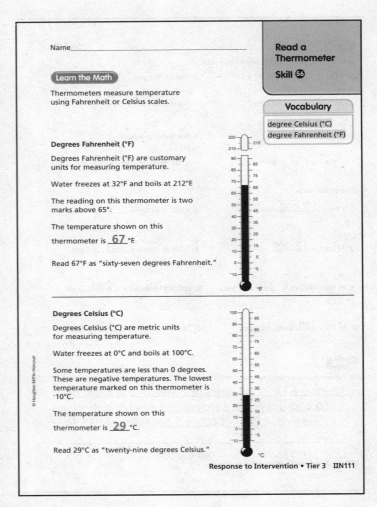

Name_____

Learn the Math

Thermometers measure temperature using Fahrenheit or Celsius scales.

Vocabulary
degree Celsius (°C)
degree Fahrenheit (°F)

Degrees Fahrenheit (°F)

Degrees Fahrenheit (°F) are customary units for measuring temperature.

Water freezes at 32°F and boils at 212°F.

The reading on this thermometer is two marks above 65°.

The temperature shown on this thermometer is __67__ °F.

Read 67°F as "sixty-seven degrees Fahrenheit."

Degrees Celsius (°C)

Degrees Celsius (°C) are metric units for measuring temperature.

Water freezes at 0°C and boils at 100°C.

Some temperatures are less than 0 degrees. These are negative temperatures. The lowest temperature marked on this thermometer is -10°C.

The temperature shown on this thermometer is __29__ °C.

Read 29°C as "twenty-nine degrees Celsius."

Response to Intervention • Tier 3 IIN111

---

thermometer that has a Fahrenheit scale and to the thermometer that has a Celsius scale.

When there are two scales shown on one thermometer, help students see that either scale can be used. Point out, however, that the readings will be different on each scale.

Remind students that when writing the temperature, the degree symbol is followed by the unit abbreviation (F or C).

Lead students to see that the temperature scales are similar to number lines; numbers on one side of zero are positive and on the other side, they are negative.

Talk Math

- **In the first problem, between which labeled marks is 85°?** 80 and 90

- **In the second problem, how do you know that the temperature is 29°C, and not 29°F?** On the Celsius scale, the mark is at 29.

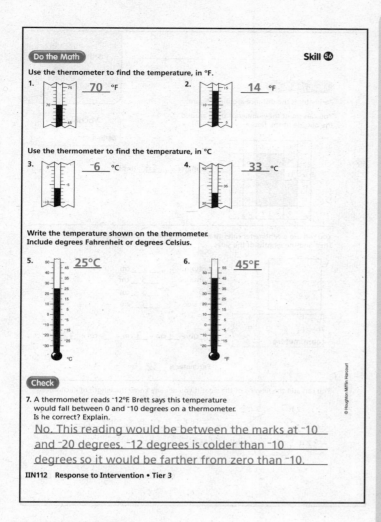

Do the Math Skill ⑤⑥

Use the thermometer to find the temperature, in °F.

1. _70_ °F

2. _14_ °F

Use the thermometer to find the temperature, in °C

3. _-6_ °C

4. _33_ °C

Write the temperature shown on the thermometer. Include degrees Fahrenheit or degrees Celsius.

5. _25°C_

6. _45°F_

Check

7. A thermometer reads -12°F. Brett says this temperature would fall between 0 and -10 degrees on a thermometer. Is he correct? Explain.

No. This reading would be between the marks at -10
and -20 degrees. -12 degrees is colder than -10
degrees so it would be farther from zero than -10.

Do the Math

Tell students that they are shown only representative parts of thermometers on student page **IIN112**, so they may not always see the zero mark. Help them to realize that negative temperatures are always represented by negative numbers, and that positive temperatures are not preceded by a + sign.

Talk Math

• In Problem 2, to which labeled mark is the reading closest? 15

• Which scale is used in Problem 5? C, Celsius

Check

Remind students that the farther above zero, the hotter the temperature, and the farther below zero, the colder the temperature. Show how a thermometer is similar to a number line.

Alternative Teaching Strategy

Temperature in Different Cities

Objective To show various temperature readings on Fahrenheit and Celsius scale thermometers

Materials grid paper, thermometer, colored pencils

• Have students use grid paper to make blank thermometer outlines. Instruct students to label a line at the bottom of the paper -10°F, then count up 10 lines, and label 0°F. Explain that each horizontal line represents one degree. Guide them to label to 100°F, taping two pieces of grid paper together as necessary. Have students make five "thermometers."

• Have them make Celsius thermometers on a separate piece of paper because the scales are not the same. Have them label the Celsius thermometers from -42°C to 68°C. Show students an actual thermometer labeled with both scales to show how they are different.

• Start by explaining that the United States uses the Fahrenheit scale. Say: **A typical temperature in Dallas in January may be 53°F.** Ask: **Between which labeled number marks is this temperature?** 50 and 60 Have students draw the temperature on a Fahrenheit scale by counting three up from 50, making a mark, and filling in the area below.

• Say: **A typical temperature in Anchorage, Alaska in January is 12°F.** Have students mark this on a Fahrenheit scale by counting two up from 10.

• Explain that other countries use the Celsius scale. Say: **A typical temperature in Oslo, Norway in January may be -1°C.** Have students mark this on a Celsius scale by counting one down from zero. Say: **The temperature in Madrid, Spain that day is 9°C.** Allow students to mark this on a Celsius scale.

• To extend the activity, have one student show a particular temperature on a thermometer, and have a partner take the reading. Students should take turns marking and making readings.

Perimeter
Skill 57

Objective
To find the perimeter of polygons with 3, 4, 5, and 6 sides

Materials
centimeter ruler, cardboard cut-out polygons (3 to 6 sides)

Vocabulary
perimeter The distance around a figure

Pre-Assess

Direct students to find the perimeters of various polygons. Provide one pentagon with given side lengths of 5, 7, 4, and 6. Tell students that the perimeter is 25 and ask: **What is the missing side length?** 3 Ask them to define *perimeter* in their own words. Ask: **How are the perimeter and the side lengths related?** The perimeter is the sum of all the side lengths.

Common Misconception

• Students may confuse *perimeter* with *area*.

• To correct this, remind them that perimeter is the distance around a figure, while area is the number of square units needed to cover a surface. Show students a 5-in. by 5-in. square drawn on grid paper and have them find both the perimeter and the area.

Ask students to identify each side of the figure in the first problem of student page **IIN113** by drawing a dark line along it. Remind students to count only the outside edges of the grid squares.

Explain to students that counting the number of units of grid squares is only one possible way to find perimeter, and it works for different figures made up of squares and rectangles.

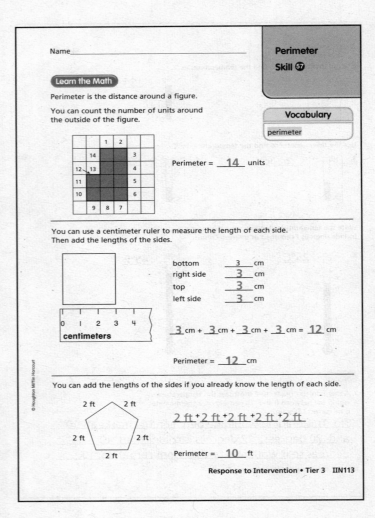

Instruct students to use centimeter rulers to find the lengths of the remaining 3 sides of the figure in the second problem. Once sides are measured, instruct students to add the lengths to find the perimeter.

Talk Math

• **What different methods can you use to find perimeter?** You can count the number of units on a grid, measure, and add the side lengths.

• **Could you find the perimeter of a rectangle if you knew only the length and width?** Yes, because opposite sides of a rectangle are equal. Help students to see that if they know the length and width of a rectangle, they can determine the measurements of all four sides.

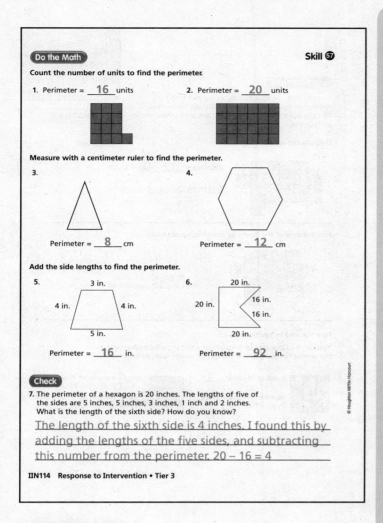

Count the number of units to find the perimeter.

1. Perimeter = __16__ units

2. Perimeter = __20__ units

Measure with a centimeter ruler to find the perimeter.

3.

Perimeter = __8__ cm

4.

Perimeter = __12__ cm

Add the side lengths to find the perimeter.

5.
3 in.
4 in.   4 in.
5 in.

Perimeter = __16__ in.

6.
20 in.
20 in.   16 in.
        16 in.
20 in.

Perimeter = __92__ in.

Check

7. The perimeter of a hexagon is 20 inches. The lengths of five of the sides are 5 inches, 5 inches, 3 inches, 1 inch and 2 inches. What is the length of the sixth side? How do you know?

The length of the sixth side is 4 inches. I found this by adding the lengths of the five sides, and subtracting this number from the perimeter. 20 – 16 = 4

Do the Math

Ask students to count the number of sides for each polygon. Remind them that the lengths of all sides must be added to find perimeter.

Talk Math

• **How many sides does the polygon in Problem 1 have?** 6 sides

• **How can you be sure that you have counted, measured, or added all of the sides?** Possible answer: make a list of the measurements of each side.

Check

You might encourage students to write an equation for finding the perimeter: 5 in. + 5 in. + 3 in. + 1 in. + 2 in. + Side 6 = 20 in.

Alternative Teaching Strategy
Measure and Add Side Lengths

Objective To find the perimeter of polygons (with 3 to 6 sides) by measuring and adding side lengths.

Materials inch or centimeter rulers, blank sheet of paper

• Students should work in pairs. Give a ruler to each pair. Draw the following table on the board for students to copy.

Number of sides = _____	
Side	Length
1	
2	
3	

Perimeter = _____

• Start by having one student from each pair draw a triangle, using the ruler as a straight edge.

• The other student in the pair should use the ruler to measure each side, and fill in the table.

• Ask: **How can you use the information about each side to find the perimeter?** Add the side lengths to find the perimeter.

• Tell the student who measured the sides to find the perimeter, and ask the partner to check the work.

• Have partners switch roles, and repeat the activity with figures that have 4, 5, and 6 sides. Guide students to make new, expanded tables to accommodate the number of sides in each figure. Ask: **Is there another way to organize information?** Possible answer: the sides could be labeled as they are measured.

Objective

To estimate and find the area of plane figures

Materials

grid paper, pencil

Vocabulary

area The number of square units needed to cover a surface

square unit A square that is 1 unit long and 1 unit wide

Pre-Assess

On grid paper, have students draw the outline of a figure that has an area of 21 square units. Tell them that the figure should be composed of squares that touch each other along at least one side. Have students shade the area of their figures. Ask: **How could you find the area of your figure?** Count the squares that are shaded. **Could your figure be a square or a rectangle?** It could be a rectangle, but it could not be a square. **What would the side lengths of a rectangle be if the area is 21 square units?** 7 units and 3 units

Common Misconception

- Students may try to find area by multiplying length and width in figures that are not rectangular.

- To correct this, remind students that the areas of rectangles and squares are found by multiplying length and width because there are always the same number of square units in each row.

Learn the Math

Have students look at student page **IIN115**. Discuss the meaning of square units with students. Guide them to see that a square unit is a square that measures 1 unit on each side. Tell students that area is always given in square units.

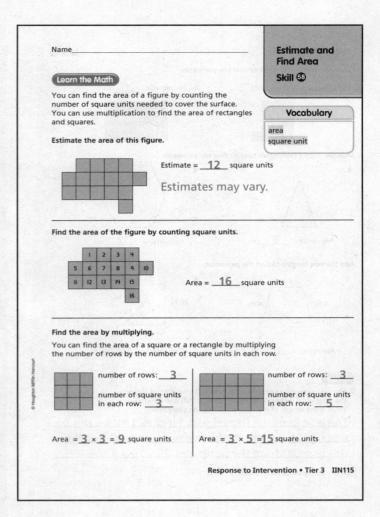

Learn the Math

You can find the area of a figure by counting the number of square units needed to cover the surface. You can use multiplication to find the area of rectangles and squares.

Vocabulary

area
square unit

Estimate the area of this figure.

Estimate = __12__ square units

Estimates may vary.

Find the area of the figure by counting square units.

Area = __16__ square units

Find the area by multiplying.

You can find the area of a square or a rectangle by multiplying the number of rows by the number of square units in each row.

number of rows: __3__

number of square units in each row: __3__

Area = $3 \times 3 = 9$ square units

number of rows: __3__

number of square units in each row: __5__

Area = $3 \times 5 = 15$ square units

Response to Intervention • Tier 3   IIN115

Explain to students that counting square units is a way to find the area of polygons that are not rectangular. Help them see that they can either count square units or use multiplication to find the area of a square or a rectangle.

Talk Math

- **How are the rows in the first figure different from the rows in the square or the rectangle?** The rows in the first figure have different numbers of square units.

- **When can multiplication be used to find area?** Multiplication can be used to find the area of plane figures such as a square and a rectangle.

- **Which numbers are multiplied to find areas of rectangles?** The number of rows and the number of square units in each row are multiplied (or, length and width are multiplied).

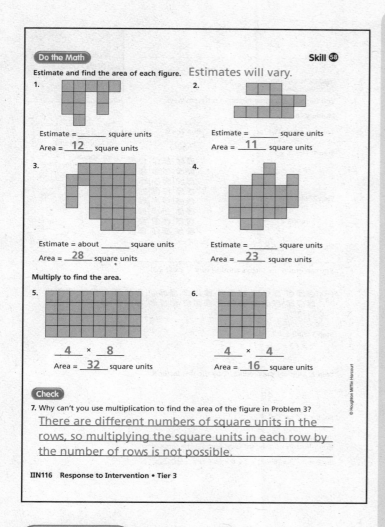

Do the Math

Estimate and find the area of each figure. Estimates will vary.

1.

Estimate = _____ square units

Area = __12__ square units

2.

Estimate = _____ square units

Area = __11__ square units

3.

Estimate = about _____ square units

Area = __28__ square units

4.

Estimate = _____ square units

Area = __23__ square units

Multiply to find the area.

5.

__4__ × __8__

Area = __32__ square units

6.

__4__ × __4__

Area = __16__ square units

Check

7. Why can't you use multiplication to find the area of the figure in Problem 3?

There are different numbers of square units in the rows, so multiplying the square units in each row by the number of rows is not possible.

© Houghton Mifflin Harcourt

Do the Math

For some students, it may be easiest to first identify which of the figures on student page **IIN116** have rectangular shapes. Stress that the areas of the figures in Problems 5 and 6 can be found using multiplication.

Talk Math

- **What method of finding area will work for all the figures?** counting square units

- **If there were 9 squares in each row in Problem 5, what would the area be?** 36 square units

Check

Ask: **When you find the area of a rectangle, what do you multiply?** The number of rows and the number of square units in each row. Ask: **In this figure, does each row have an equal number of square units?** no

---

Alternative Teaching Strategy

Find area of plane figures

Objective To create and measure the area of plane figures

Materials square tiles, grid paper

- Divide students into pairs.

- Pass out 16 square tiles to each student pair. Tell students that each tile is a square unit. Discuss the meaning of *square unit* with the class.

- Have one student from each pair use all the tiles to make a rectangle.

- Ask: **How can you find the area of a rectangle?** by counting square units or by multiplying Have the second student of the pair find the area.

- Ask: **Why can multiplication be used to find the area of your rectangle?** Since the square tiles make an array, each row of the array has the same number of tiles.

- Next have student pairs use all the tiles to make a figure that is not rectangular.

- Ask: **How can you find the area of a plane figure that is not rectangular?** by counting the tiles **Can you use multiplication to find the area?** no

- Have students find the area of this figure. Ask: **Can two figures with different shapes have the same area?** yes

- Give students time to make figures using various numbers of tiles. For each figure, one partner should determine all possible methods for finding the area. The other partner should then find the area. Have students use grid paper to record the figures and areas.

Objective
To use the Associative Property of Multiplication to multiply three factors

Materials
grid paper

Vocabulary
Associative Property of Multiplication (Grouping Property) The property that states you can group factors in different ways and still get the same product

Parentheses Symbols used in an expression to show which operation or operations should be completed first

Pre-Assess
Show students the number sentence 3 × 2 × 4. Instruct students to rewrite the sentence twice, using parentheses to group the factors a different way each time. Ask: **What happens to the product if you group the factors in different ways?** The product stays the same. You might encourage students to draw arrays to illustrate each grouping.

Common Misconception
- Students may always choose to group the first two factors.

- To correct this, tell them that the factors can be grouped in different ways: the first factor may be grouped with the second factor or the second and third factors may be grouped together. Guide them to choose a grouping based on basic facts.

Learn the Math

Explain to students that the Associative Property of Multiplication states that the grouping of factors in a multiplication problem does not affect the product.

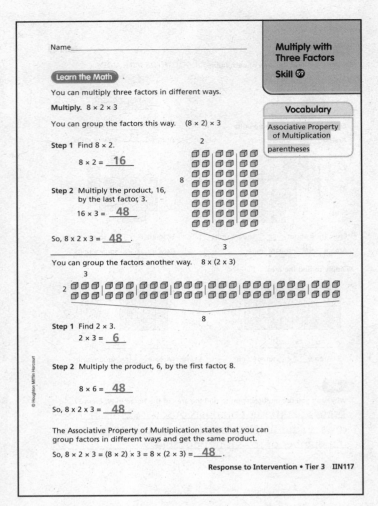

Help students relate each of the arrays on student page IIN117 to the grouping of the factors. Remind them to count rows and columns and to compare the number of cubes in each array to see that the total number is the same. Help them see that one grouping may make the problem easier to solve. For example, (8 × 2) × 3 = 16 × 3 = 48 may be more difficult than 8 × (2 × 3) = 8 × 6 = 48 because multiplying 8 and 6 may be easier to multiply than multiplying 16 and 3.

Talk Math

- **What do parentheses represent?** a grouping of factors

- **Does the placement of parentheses change the product?** no

Do the Math

Use parentheses to show how you can group the factors. Write the multiplication sentence and solve. Possible groupings are shown.

1. $3 \times 5 \times 7 = \underline{105}$
   $(3 \times 5) \times 7$
   $3 \times 5 = \underline{15}$
   $15 \times 7 = \underline{105}$

2. $6 \times 1 \times 4 = \underline{24}$
   $(6 \times 1) \times 4$
   $6 \times 1 = 6$
   $6 \times 4 = 24$

3. $8 \times 4 \times 2 = \underline{64}$
   $8 \times (4 \times 2)$
   $4 \times 2 = 8$
   $8 \times 8 = 64$

4. $2 \times 8 \times 4 = \underline{64}$
   $(2 \times 8) \times 4$
   $2 \times 8 = 16$
   $16 \times 4 = 64$

5. $7 \times 1 \times 2 = \underline{14}$
   $(7 \times 1) \times 2 = 14$
   $7 \times 1 = 7$
   $7 \times 2 = 14$

6. $4 \times 5 \times 5 = \underline{100}$
   $4 \times (5 \times 5)$
   $5 \times 5 = 25$
   $4 \times 25 = 100$

7. $4 \times 5 \times 6 = \underline{120}$
   $(4 \times 5) \times 6$
   $4 \times 5 = 20$
   $20 \times 6 = 120$

8. $9 \times 6 \times 3 = \underline{162}$
   $9 \times (6 \times 3)$
   $6 \times 3 = 18$
   $9 \times 18 = 162$

Check

9. Use parentheses to show two ways to group the factors in the multiplication problem below. Then explain how to find the product for each grouping.

$3 \times 3 \times 8$

$(3 \times 3) \times 8$: _multiply 3 and 3, then multiply the_ _product, 9, by 8;_

$3 \times (3 \times 8)$: _multiply 3 and 8, then multiply the_ _product, 24, by 3._

$3 \times 3 \times 8 = \underline{72}$

Do the Math

Help students to understand that parentheses can be placed around the first and second factors, or the second and third factors in the problems on student page **IIN118**. Encourage students to choose the grouping that will simplify the problem for them.

Talk Math

- **What three factors are in Problem 3?** 8, 4, and 2

- **What are two different ways of grouping the factors?** 8 and 4 may be grouped together with parentheses, or 4 and 2 may be grouped together.

Check

Guide students to recognize that choosing to group 3 and 3 may help them more quickly find the product.

Alternative Teaching Strategy

Use the Associative Property of Multiplication

Objective To use the Associative Property of Multiplication to multiply three factors

Materials number cube

- Write ___ × ___ × ___ = ___ on the board. Toss a number cube three times. Fill the blank spaces in order with the three numbers.

- Ask: **How could you draw parentheses to group two of the numbers together?** Possible answer: you could place parentheses around the first two numbers. Place parentheses, and then have students find the product. They may also draw arrays on grid paper to help them solve the problem.

- Ask: **How else could you draw parentheses to group two of the numbers together?** Possible answer: you could place parentheses around the last two numbers. Rewrite the problem with the new grouping, and have students find the product.

- Ask: **Are the products the same or different?** They are the same. Guide students to see that different groupings do not change the product.

- Instruct student groups to repeat the activity several times with their own number cubes. Ask them to find two ways to group their factors each time. Encourage them to choose a grouping based on facts that they know best.

Explore Volume
Skill ⑥⓪

Objective
To find the volume of prisms by counting and adding

Materials
inch or centimeter cubes

Vocabulary
volume The measure of the amount of space a solid figure occupies

cubic unit A unit of volume with dimensions of 1 unit × 1 unit × 1 unit

Pre-Assess
Ask students to define volume. Show them a rectangular prism constructed from inch or centimeter cubes. Ask: **How can you find the volume of this prism?** Possible answers: Count the number of total cubes; count the cubes in each layer, and add the layers together; multiply length × width × height. **Tell students to determine the volume of the prism.**

Common Misconception
• When determining volume, students may only count the cubes that make up the front face of the prism.

• To correct this, review the difference between volume and area. Make sure students understand that they must count all the cubes that make up the figure.

Learn the Math

Explain to students that volume is a measure of the amount of space inside a solid. Tell them that it is measured in cubic units, such as cubic inches (in.³), cubic centimeters (cm³) or cubic feet (ft³). Call students' attention to the cubic unit illustration at the top of student page **IIN119**. Guide students to see that the dimensions of a cubic unit are always 1 unit × 1 unit × 1 unit.

The second problem introduces the idea of counting all cubic units that fit into a prism to

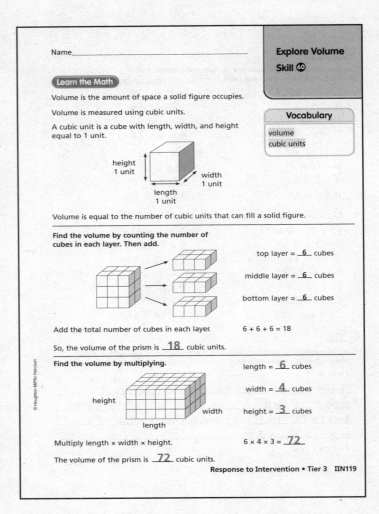

find volume. Remind students that all cubes need to be counted, even the ones that are not visible in the drawing. Help them determine both the number of cubes in each layer, and the number of layers of cubes. Tell them to add the layers together. Encourage students to use actual cubes to build a three-dimensional version of the prism.

For the third problem, find the length, width, and height. Then multiply l × w × h to find volume. Students may also use actual cubes to build the rectangular prism.

Talk Math

• **In the second problem, how many cubes are in the middle layer of the prism?** 6

• **In the third problem, how many cubes are in each layer of the prism?** 24

• **How do you know how many cubes are in the bottom layer?** Since it is a rectangular prism, the same number would have to be on the bottom layer as the other layers.

© Houghton Mifflin Harcourt

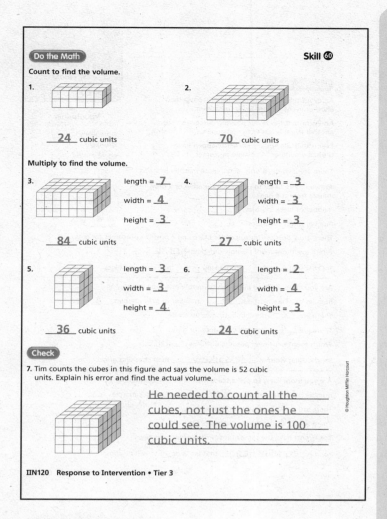

Do the Math

Skill 60

Count to find the volume.

1. **24** cubic units

2. **70** cubic units

Multiply to find the volume.

3. length = **7**
   width = **4**
   height = **3**
   84 cubic units

4. length = **3**
   width = **3**
   height = **3**
   27 cubic units

5. length = **3**
   width = **3**
   height = **4**
   36 cubic units

6. length = **2**
   width = **4**
   height = **3**
   24 cubic units

Check

7. Tim counts the cubes in this figure and says the volume is 52 cubic units. Explain his error and find the actual volume.

He needed to count all the cubes, not just the ones he could see. The volume is 100 cubic units.

IIN120   Response to Intervention • Tier 3

Do the Math

For all problems on student page **IIN120**, ask students to give the number of cubes in each layer and the number of layers of cubes in each figure. Remind students that all cubes need to be counted to find volume.

Talk Math

- **In Problem 3, how many cubes are in each layer?** 28

- **In Problem 5, how many layers of cubes are there?** 4

Check

Ask: **Did the student count every cube?** No, he only counted the ones he could see. **How many cubes are in each layer?** 25 **How many layers are there?** 4

Alternative Teaching Strategy

Guess and Check Volume

Objective To explore volume of prisms

Materials centimeter cubes, nets for rectangular prisms measuring 2 cm × 3 cm × 5 cm and 4 cm × 2 cm × 2 cm box as shown below, scissors

- Divide students into groups and show them how to make boxes by cutting out and folding nets. Tell them to label the 2 × 3 × 5 rectangular prism *Box A*, and the 4 × 2 × 2 rectangular prism *Box B*. Explain that the top is left off the box so it can be filled with cubes.

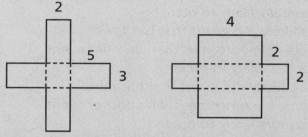

- Tell students that they will be estimating and finding volume. Explain that each of their cubes represents a cubic unit, which is a unit of measure for volume. Ask: **How many cubes do you think will fit into Box A?** Tell students to write down their estimates.

- Instruct students to find the volume of *Box A* by placing centimeter cubes inside the net and counting the number of cubes that fit inside, with no space left over. Ask: **What is the volume?** 30 cubic units Ask students to say whether their estimates were close to the actual volume.

- Ask: **How many cubes do you think will fit in Box B?** Tell students to record estimates, and then determine the actual volume of *Box B* using the same method as that for *Box A*. Ask: **What is the volume?** 16 cubic units

- Next ask one student in each group to use the centimeter cubes to make a rectangular prism. Ask the other students to estimate and find the number of layers of cubes, the number of cubes in each layer, and the total number of cubes. Have students alternate building prisms and recording the height, width, length (in units) and volume (in cubic units).

Response to Intervention • Tier 3   IIN120

Objective
To compare likelihoods of events

Materials
number cube labeled 1 to 6

Vocabulary
equally likely Events that have the same number of possible outcomes are *equally likely* to occur

less likely An event that has fewer possible outcomes than another event is *less likely* to occur

more likely An event that has more possible outcomes than another event is *more likely* to occur

Pre-Assess
Have students look at a number cube labeled 1 to 6. Ask: **How many numbers on the cube are even? How many are odd?** 3 are even; 3 are odd Ask: **Is there a greater likelihood of tossing an odd number or a greater likelihood of tossing an even number? Explain.** Tossing an even number is as equally likely as tossing an odd number because there are the same number of outcomes for each event. Ask students to come up with an event that is more likely than tossing an odd number, and an event that is less likely than tossing an even number.

Common Misconception
- Students may have difficulty determining the number of possible outcomes for one event.
- To correct this, have students first identify and write all the possible outcomes that could happen. For example, when tossing a number cube there are six possible outcomes: tossing a 1, 2, 3, 4, 5 or 6. Then have the students write the possible outcomes for one event and count them. For example, if the event is "toss an odd number," the possible outcomes are 1, 3, 5. There are three possible outcomes for this event.

Name_____

Learn the Math

An event that has more possible outcomes than another event is *more likely* to happen.

An event that has fewer possible outcomes than another event is *less likely* to happen.

Events that are *equally likely* to happen have the same number of possible outcomes

Vocabulary
more likely
less likely
equally likely

There are 2 white, 4 gray, and 2 black marbles in a bag.

Are you more likely to pull a black marble or a gray marble from the bag?

number of black marbles __2__

number of gray marbles __4__

There are 2 possible outcomes for black and 4 possible outcomes for gray.

Which event has more possible outcomes? __gray__

So, choosing gray is ___more likely___ than choosing black.

Are you more likely to pull a white marble or a gray marble?

number of white marbles __2__   number of gray marbles __4__

There are __2__ possible outcomes for white.

There are __4__ possible outcomes for gray.

Which event has fewer possible outcomes? __white__

So, choosing white is ___less likely___ than choosing gray.

Are you more likely to pull a black marble or a white marble?

number of white marbles __2__   number of black marbles __2__

There are __2__ possible outcomes for white.

There are __2__ possible outcomes for black.

The events have the same number of possible outcomes.

So, it is ___equally likely___ that black or white will be chosen.

Response to Intervention · Tier 3   IIN121

Learn the Math

Guide students through each problem on student page IIN121. Help them to see that there is an order to solving the problems: 1) identify the events you are to compare 2) count the possible outcomes for each event, 3) compare the number of possible outcomes and 4) decide if one event is more likely or less likely than the other.

Talk Math

- **Which colors are you comparing in the first problem?** black and gray

- **Do you need to look at white marbles in this problem? Why or why not?** No, it is not one of the colors to be compared.

Tell students to compare only two events at a time.

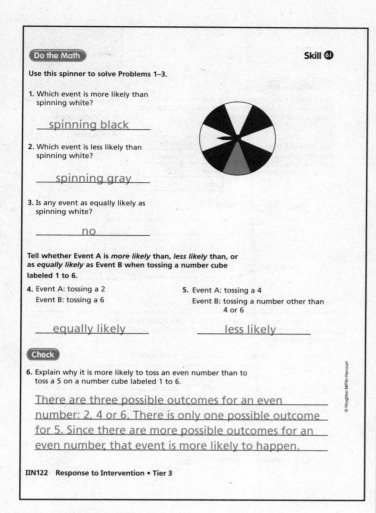

The worksheet image (IIN122) shows:

Do the Math — Skill 61

Use this spinner to solve Problems 1–3.

1. Which event is more likely than spinning white?

   spinning black

2. Which event is less likely than spinning white?

   spinning gray

3. Is any event as equally likely as spinning white?

   _no_

Tell whether Event A is *more likely* than, *less likely* than, or as *equally likely* as Event B when tossing a number cube labeled 1 to 6.

4. Event A: tossing a 2
   Event B: tossing a 6

   equally likely

5. Event A: tossing a 4
   Event B: tossing a number other than 4 or 6

   less likely

Check

6. Explain why it is more likely to toss an even number than to toss a 5 on a number cube labeled 1 to 6.

   There are three possible outcomes for an even number: 2, 4 or 6. There is only one possible outcome for 5. Since there are more possible outcomes for an even number, that event is more likely to happen.

IIN122 Response to Intervention • Tier 3

Do the Math

As students complete student page **IIN122**, tell them to write down their thoughts in order to keep them organized. For every event they consider, they should write the number of possible outcomes.

Talk Math

• **In Problem 5, how many possible outcomes are there for the event "tossing a 4?"** 1 possible outcome

• **How many possible outcomes are there for the event "tossing a number other than 4 or 6?"** 4 possible outcomes

Check

Tell students to write down all possible outcomes for each event. For the event "toss a 5" there is one possible outcome, 5. For the event "toss an even number" there are three possible outcomes: 2, 4, 6. Ask them to define *more likely*.

Alternative Teaching Strategy

Compare Likelihoods of Events

Objective To decide if an event is more likely than, less likely than or as equally likely as another event to occur

Materials number cube labeled 1 to 6

• Give number cubes to student pairs. Write this table on the board for students to copy. Leave space for several rows.

Event	Possible Outcomes	Number of Possible Outcomes
Toss a 2	2	1
Toss a 4 or 6	4, 6	2

• Ask: **How many possible outcomes are there for tossing the number 2?** 1 **How many possible outcomes are there for tossing a 4 or a 6?** 2 Help students fill in their tables.

• Ask: **Is tossing a 2 more likely than tossing a 4 or a 6?** no **Explain.** Possible answer: There is only one way to toss a 2 and there are two ways to toss a 4 or 6. So, tossing a 4 or 6 is more likely.

• Explain that when you compare likelihoods of events occurring you compare the number of possible outcomes for each event (column 3 of the table). Ask: **Is there any event that is as equally likely as tossing a 2?** Yes, for example, tossing a 5.

• Ask one student from a pair to choose an event and write it in the table. Give them examples, such as "toss an even number" or "toss a number other than 5." Tell students to compare the two events, and determine which is more likely.

• Ask the students to find events that are equally likely to happen, and allow them to share their findings with the class.

Response to Intervention • Tier 3   IIN122

Tree Diagrams
Skill 62

Objective
To record combinations in a tree diagram

Vocabulary
combination A choice of items in which the order does not matter

tree diagram An organized list that shows all possible combinations of items

Pre-Assess

Give students the fruit and cheese information below. Ask them to find all fruit and cheese combinations using a tree diagram. Ask them to explain their work.

Fruit options: pear, banana
Cheese options: swiss, cheddar, provolone
Ask: **What are the possible combinations?** pear, swiss; pear, cheddar; pear, provolone; banana, swiss; banana, cheddar; banana, provolone

Common Misconception

• When making a tree diagram, students may not list all choices in the second group next to each item in the first group.

• To correct this, remind students that the exact same items should be listed next to each choice from the first group. As a check, tell them to make sure that each item from the first group has the same number of branches connected to it.

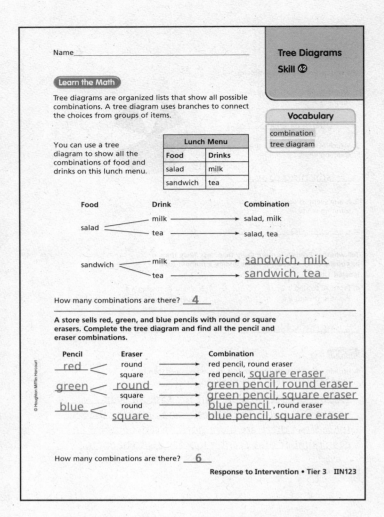

Learn the Math

Explain to students the meaning of a *combination*. Tell them that in a combination, the order of items is not important.

Use the first problem on student page **IIN123** to show students different parts of a tree diagram. All the items from one group are listed at the far left. Explain that branches connect the items from the first group to choices from the second group.

Note that all the items in the second group are listed next to each item from the first group. Milk and tea are both listed next to salad, and both are listed again next to sandwich. Help students name combinations by grouping items connected by a branch.

Guide students to complete the tree diagram for the second problem. Remind them to list the items from the first group (pencils) at the far left. Ask them to count all branches and all combinations.

You may also wish to show students that the number of choices in the first group multiplied by the number of choices in the second group is equal to the total number of combinations.

Talk Math

• **How many different kinds of pencils are there in the second problem?** 3 kinds of pencils

• **Would there be more or fewer combinations if there were two kinds of pencils?** fewer

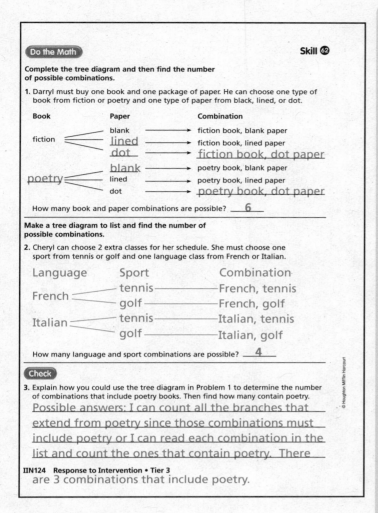

Do the Math

Do the Math

For the problems on student page **IIN124**, remind students of the purpose of branches in a tree diagram. Remind them that every possible combination is listed in a tree diagram that is drawn correctly.

Talk Math

- **For Problem 2, how many language choices are there?** 2 language choices

- **How many sports should be listed next to each language choice?** 2 sports

Check

Explain that there are a variety of methods for counting the combinations that contain a specific item, including counting branches, or circling the combinations in the list that apply.

Alternative Teaching Strategy

Make a Tree Diagram

Objective To make a model of a tree diagram and use it to find combinations

Materials 3 blue squares, 3 yellow squares, 3 black squares, 3 red circles, 3 green circles, 3 white circles, 9 1-ft lengths of string, paper and pencil

- Show all the squares and circles to students. Tell them that you will work together to find out how many square and circle combinations are possible.

- Ask: **How many different colors of squares are there?** three colors Place three different-colored squares a short distance apart from each other on the floor at the front of the room.

- Ask: **How many different colors of circles are there?** three colors **Which circle colors could be combined with one color of square?** red, green, or white

- Place the circles in a pile. Ask one student at a time to pick up a circle, choose a square to set it in front of, and connect it to this square with a piece of string.

- When they are finished, draw students' attention to how the pattern on the floor resembles a tree, and that the different groups (circles, squares) are at different parts of the tree. Guide students to make a tree diagram using the floor pattern as a template.

- Tell students that the lines (strings) group two choices together to make a combination. Ask the class to say the combinations one at a time, and write them in their tree diagrams.

- Modify the activity by placing three circles, one of each color, at the front of the room, and connecting them to the squares reversing the tree diagram. Help students to see that all of the same combinations will be found. Tell them that the combination red circle, blue square is the same as the combination blue square, red circle.